Summer Solutions.
Minutes a Day–Mastery for a Lifetime!

Algebra I
Part B

Mathematics

3rd Edition

Nancy McGraw

Simple Solutions Learning, Inc.
Beachwood, OH

Summer Solutions

Algebra I, Part B

Mathematics

3rd Edition

Printed in the United States of America

ISBN: 978-1-934210-40-6

United States coin images from the United States Mint

Cover Design: Randy Reetz
Editor: Lauren Dambrogio

Instructions for Parents/Guardians

- *Summer Solutions* is an extension of the *Simple Solutions* Approach being used by thousands of children in schools across the United States.

- The 30 lessons included in each workbook are meant to review and reinforce the skills learned in the grade level just completed.

- The program is designed to be used three days per week for ten weeks to ensure retention.

- Completing the book all at one time defeats the purpose of sustained practice over the summer break.

- This book contains lesson answers in the back.

- This book also contains a "Who Knows?" drill and Help Pages that list vocabulary, solved examples, formulas, and measurement conversions.

- Lessons should be checked immediately for optimal feedback. Items that were difficult or done incorrectly should be resolved to ensure mastery.

- Adjust the use of the book to fit your summer schedule. More lessons may have to be completed during some weeks.

Summer Solutions Algebra I, Part B

Reviewed Skills

- Slope & Equation of a Line
- Solving Systems by Elimination & Substitution
- Linear Inequalities
- Zero and Negative Exponents
- Scientific Notation
- Multiplication & Division Properties of Exponents
- Adding & Subtracting Polynomials
- Factoring Polynomials
- Factoring Perfect Squares
- Solving Quadratic Equations
- Using the Quadratic Formula
- Radical Theory and Simplifying Radicals
- Addition & Subtraction of Radicals
- Operations with Rational Expressions
- Solving Rational Equations
- Pythagorean Theorem

Help Pages begin on page 63.

Answers to Lessons begin on page 89.

Lesson #1

1. What is the value of 3^5?

2. Solve for x. $4 > -2 + x > -5$

3. $-96 + (-49) = ?$

4. Write 3.26×10^4 in standard notation.

5. Multiply. $3x(4x^2 + 3x - 8)$

6. Determine the slope of a line passing through (2, 1) and (6, 8).

7. Simplify. $\dfrac{(4x^2)^3}{10x^4}$

8. Find the perimeter of the rectangle.

$4a + 1$

$2a$

9. Multiply. $(x^{-8}y^{-5})(x^{10}y^{-2})$

10. Find $\frac{2}{5}$ of 55.

11. $6\frac{1}{5} + 3\frac{3}{4} = ?$

12. Multiply. $(8d - 4)(8d + 4)$

13. How many decades are 60 years?

14. Simplify. $5\sqrt{81b^{30}}$

15. Simplify. $9\sqrt{2} - 3\sqrt{2}$

16. Solve the system of equations. $\begin{aligned} 2x + 7y &= 16 \\ -2x + 8y &= 14 \end{aligned}$

17. Simplify. $4\sqrt{75} + 6\sqrt{27}$

18. Simplify. $\dfrac{-3a^2b^3c}{-27abc}$

19. Simplify. $\dfrac{(4y)^0}{(7y)^0}$

20. Find the sum. $\begin{aligned} 9a^3 + 10a^2 - 4a + 4 \\ + \ \ 4a^3 \qquad\qquad - 5a - 3 \end{aligned}$

1.	2.	3.	4.
5.	6.	7.	8.
9.	10.	11.	12.
13.	14.	15.	16.
17.	18.	19.	20.

Lesson #2

1. Simplify. $(5x^2y^3z^4)^2$

2. $20 + 2 \cdot 4 + 10 \div 2 - 1 = ?$

3. Simplify. $6a^{-3}b^2c^{-1}$

4. Solve for x. $-6x = 84$

5. Find the area of a triangle if the base is 33 cm and the height is 8 cm.

6. The freezing temperature of water is _____ degrees Fahrenheit.

7. Simplify. $3\sqrt{25xy} + 4\sqrt{36xy} - 2\sqrt{81xy}$

8. $22\frac{2}{7} - 16\frac{4}{7} = ?$

9. $\frac{-90}{-2} = ?$

10. Simplify. $-6\sqrt{49y^{22}}$

11. Factor. $9k^2 - 25$

12. $0.63 \times 0.03 = ?$

13. Solve for h. $h + 7 \leq 16$

14. Write 0.0000812 in scientific notation.

15. Evaluate $4a(a + b)$ when $a = 3$ and $b = 4$.

16. A triangle with two congruent sides is a(n) _____ triangle.

17. Simplify. $-3\sqrt{28x^3y^7}$

18. What number is 40% of 80?

19. $\begin{pmatrix} 7 & -3 & 2 \\ 6 & 4 & -8 \end{pmatrix} - \begin{pmatrix} 5 & -2 & 0 \\ -1 & 3 & -5 \end{pmatrix} = ?$

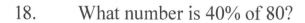

5 m

3 m

8 m

20. Calculate the surface area of the rectangular prism.

1.	2.	3.	4.
5.	6.	7.	8.
9.	10.	11.	12.
13.	14.	15.	16.
17.	18.	19.	20.

Lesson #3

1.   Simplify. $(m^3 n^2)^6$

2.   A nine-sided polygon is called a(n) _____.

3.   Write 6,340,000,000 in scientific notation.

4.   Multiply. $3a(4a + 1)$

5.   Simplify. $(2x^4 z)(-4y^3 z)$

6.   The slope of a vertical line is _____.

7.   Find the area of a circle whose radius is 7 inches.

8.   Solve for a. $a + 66 = 91$

9.   Simplify. $\sqrt{18} + \sqrt{3}$

10.   Multiply. $(x^2 - 3)(x^2 + 4)$

11.   Simplify. $\sqrt{49x^4 y^6}$

12. $5 \cdot 7 + 4 \cdot 5 - 12 \div 4 = ?$

13.   Write the quadratic formula.

14.   Solve for x. $\frac{x}{14} = -8$

15. $\frac{7}{9} \times \frac{27}{28} = ?$

16.   Find the area of the square.

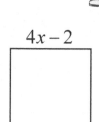

$4x - 2$

17. $-63 + (+15) + (+25) = ?$

18.   Find the y–values in the equation, $y = -5x + 1$, when $x = \{0, -2, 4\}$.

19.   Factor. $y^2 + 17y + 72$

20.   Find the difference. $16x^3 - 9x^2 + 4x - 3$
                              $-\ 9x^3 \qquad\quad -2x + 5$

1.	2.	3.	4.
5.	6.	7.	8.
9.	10.	11.	12.
13.	14.	15.	16.
17.	18.	19.	20.

Lesson #4

1. Simplify. $\sqrt{2}(5-\sqrt{8})$

2. Factor. $y^2 + 2y - 15$

3. Solve the system of equations. $\begin{aligned} x + 4y &= 14 \\ 6x - 2y &= 6 \end{aligned}$

4. Multiply. $3x(3x^2 - 7x + 4)$

5. Simplify. $4^{-2}a^2b^{-3}c^{-2}$

6. Solve for x. $7x - 9 = 3x + 19$

7. Find the area of the trapezoid.

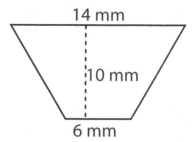

8. Solve for a. $2a + 14 = 26$

9. Jeffery's new tablet costs $280. The sales tax was 8%. What was the total cost of the laptop?

10. Simplify. $(8a^4b^2c)^2$

11. $75 + (-38) = ?$

12. Simplify. $\sqrt{3}(\sqrt{15} + \sqrt{4})$

13. $600{,}000 - 421{,}986 = ?$

14. Simplify. $6\sqrt{16x^{14}y^{40}}$

15. Write 0.00065 in scientific notation.

16. Solve for x. $\frac{2}{-3}x = 18$

17. What is the value of x in $\frac{5}{8} = \frac{x}{96}$?

18. Put these decimals in decreasing order.

    5.43   5.4   5.05   5.043

19. Solve the inequality for x. $2x - 8 \geq 10$

20. Find the sum. $(14x^3 - 7x^2 - 6x + 4) + (9x^3 + 3x - 2)$

1.	2.	3.	4.
5.	6.	7.	8.
9.	10.	11.	12.
13.	14.	15.	16.
17.	18.	19.	20.

Lesson #5

1.   Find the percent of change from 16 inches to 20 inches.

2.   Write 32% as a decimal and as a reduced fraction.

3. $98 - (-47) = ?$

4.   Evaluate $3x - y$ if $x = 6$ and $y = 3$.

5.   Write an expression that represents fifteen more than a number.

6.   What is the value of x? $-5x = 75$

7.   Solve for x. $3x - 5 \leq 10$

8.   Write the quadratic formula.

9.   Simplify. $(3a^2b^3)^3$

10. $42\frac{2}{5} - 27\frac{4}{5} = ?$

11.   Write 6.5×10^{-5} in standard notation.

12.   Multiply. $(3x^2 + 5x - 4)(x + 3)$

13.   80% of what number is 32?

14.   Simplify. $\frac{5x^{-5}}{8y^{-2}}$

15.   Find the values for y in the equation, $y = 2x - 4$, when $x = \{-5, 3, 0\}$.

16. $\frac{5}{8} \cdot \frac{12}{25} = ?$

17. $\begin{pmatrix} 9 & -3 \\ 0 & 6 \end{pmatrix} + \begin{pmatrix} 5 & -8 \\ -3 & -4 \end{pmatrix} = ?$

18.   A triangle with no sides congruent is called a(n) _____ triangle.

19.   Solve using elimination. $\begin{aligned} 3x - 2y &= 6 \\ 5x + 7y &= 41 \end{aligned}$

20.   Find the difference. $\begin{aligned} 11a^3 + 7a^2 - 4a + 5 \\ - \quad 4a^3 \qquad\qquad 2a - 7 \end{aligned}$

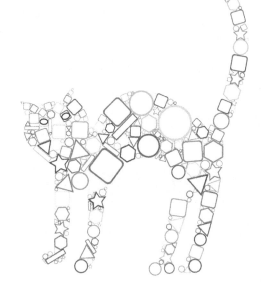

1.	2.	3.	4.
5.	6.	7.	8.
9.	10.	11.	12.
13.	14.	15.	16.
17.	18.	19.	20.

Lesson #6

1.   Factor. $5x^2 - 10x$

2.   Write 0.0000038 in scientific notation.

3.   Simplify. $\dfrac{h^{-9}}{h^{-4}}$

4.   25% of 60 is what number?

5.   Find the product. $6c(c^2 - 4c + 2)$

6.   Solve for t. $10t + 6 = 8t + 12$

7.   Solve the proportion for x. $\dfrac{5}{9} = \dfrac{x}{135}$

8.   Multiply. $(4y + 5)(4y - 5)$

9. $-83 + (-37) = ?$

10.   Solve for a. $2a - 5 \geq a + 3$

11.   Simplify. $\sqrt{81a^{10}}$

12.   Factor. $b^2 - 6b - 27$

13.   How many quarts are in 16 gallons?

14.   Find the slope of a line through points (2, 5) and (6, 8).

15.   Find the percent of change from 8 feet to 10 feet.

16.   A bag contains 6 red marbles and 8 white marbles. What is the probability of picking (red, red) with replacement of the marble before the second pick?

17.   Find the area of a parallelogram if its base is 19 centimeters and its height is 5 centimeters.

18.   Factor. $a^2 - 16$

19.   Simplify. $5x^2 y\sqrt{24x^5 y^7}$

20.   Find the sum. $\begin{array}{r} 13x^2 - 8x + 9 \\ + \ 6x^2 \qquad -7 \\ \hline \end{array}$

1.	2.	3.	4.
5.	6.	7.	8.
9.	10.	11.	12.
13.	14.	15.	16.
17.	18.	19.	20.

Lesson #7

1. Evaluate $\dfrac{ab}{3} + c$ if $a = 7$, $b = 12$, and $c = 4$.

2. Solve. $42 \div 7 + 3 \cdot 5 - 2$

3. Multiply. $(x - 6)(x + 2)$

4. Simplify. $\sqrt{25a^{10}b^{14}}$

5. Write 2.9×10^{-3} in standard notation.

6. Solve for y. $9y - 18 = 3y$

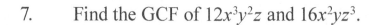

7. Find the GCF of $12x^3y^2z$ and $16x^2yz^3$.

8. Simplify. $c^4 d^3 c^{-2}$

9. Solve for x. $3x - 5 \leq 19$

10. What is the P(1, 4, 2) on three rolls of a die?

11. Factor. $a^2 + 15a + 54$

12. Write the slope and y–intercept for the line whose equation is $y = -5x + 2$.

13. Simplify. $-|-81|$

14. Simplify. $2\sqrt{18a^9}$

15. $70 - (-25) = ?$

16. Simplify. $5\sqrt{3} + 7\sqrt{3}$

17. Use the quadratic formula to solve. $a^2 - 9a + 14 = 0$.

18. Solve for c. $c + 56 = -92$

19. $-19 + (-13) + 17 = ?$

20. Simplify. $\dfrac{\sqrt{35}}{\sqrt{5}}$

1.	2.	3.	4.
5.	6.	7.	8.
9.	10.	11.	12.
13.	14.	15.	16.
17.	18.	19.	20.

Lesson #8

1.   Simplify. $3\sqrt{4} \cdot 5\sqrt{5}$

2.   25% of 60 is what number?

3.   Factor. $k^2 - 64$

4.   Write the formula for finding the volume of a cylinder.

5. $(-7)(2)(-3) = ?$

6.   A set of antique dishes cost $950. The sales tax was 8%. How much money did the antique dealer spend on the dishes?

7.   Solve using the quadratic formula. $a^2 - 9a + 8 = 0$

8.   Multiply. $(4x + 2)(2x + 3)$

9.   Solve for x. $\frac{4}{9} = \frac{x}{108}$

10. $\frac{4}{7} \cdot \frac{14}{16} = ?$

11.   Solve for a. $5(a + 2) = 40$

12.   Write 7.16×10^4 in standard notation.

13.   Simplify. $10x^{-3}y^2z^{-5}$

14.   Which is greater, $\frac{6}{25}$ or 30%?

15.   How many centimeters are in 13 meters?

16.   Simplify. $7\sqrt{16a^{20}}$

17.   Write the slope of a line that passes through points (1, 3) and (6, 8).

18.   Factor. $3x^3 + 9x^2 - 12x$

19.   Put these integers in decreasing order. $-88, \ -11, \ 0, \ -4, \ -31$

20.   Find the difference.
$$\begin{array}{r} 9x^2 - 6 \\ -\ 4x^2 + 1 \\ \hline \end{array}$$

1.	2.	3.	4.
5.	6.	7.	8.
9.	10.	11.	12.
13.	14.	15.	16.
17.	18.	19.	20.

Lesson #9

1. Solve for y. $4y + 2 = 5y + 4$

2. Write 827,000 in scientific notation.

3. Solve for x. $\frac{x}{5} + 8 = 11$

4. Factor out the GCF. $8a^3b + 16a^4b^3 - 4ab^2$

5. Write 0.36 as a percent and as a reduced fraction.

6. Round 23.359 to the nearest tenth.

7. Multiply. $(4x^2 + 2x + 3)(3x + 4)$

8. Write the slope-intercept form of a linear equation.

9. Simplify. $6n^4 \cdot 3n^5$

10. Factor. $m^2 - 6m - 40$

11. Solve. $30 + 6(3 + 2 \cdot 4 + 1)$

12. $16\frac{2}{7} - 9\frac{6}{7} = ?$

13. Evaluate $4xy + xy$ if $x = 3$ and $y = 2$.

14. $76 + (-43) = ?$

15. $\begin{pmatrix} 8 & 0 & -2 \\ 5 & 6 & 4 \end{pmatrix} + \begin{pmatrix} 3 & -5 & -7 \\ 8 & -1 & 1 \end{pmatrix} = ?$

16. Multiply. $3a(4a^2 - 3a + 5)$

17. Graph the solution for $2h + 6 \leq 18$ on a number line.

18. What is the percent of change from 21 yards to 35 yards? Round your answer to the nearest percent.

19. Calculate the circumference of a circle if its diameter is 12 feet.

20. Simplify. $\dfrac{c^{-7}d^3}{c^3d}$

1.	2.	3.	4.
5.	6.	7.	8.
9.	10.	11.	12.
13.	14.	15.	16.
17.	18.	19.	20.

Lesson #10

1. Multiply. $(x + 7)(x - 4)$

2. Solve using the system using any method. $\begin{aligned} x - 3y &= -3 \\ x + 3y &= 9 \end{aligned}$

3. What is 60% of 70?

4. Find the perimeter of the rectangle.

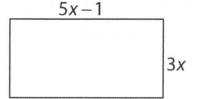

5. $66 + (-18) = ?$

6. Solve for c. $c - 19 = -40$

7. $6.43 \times 0.04 = ?$

8. Write 4,000,000,000 in scientific notation.

9. Solve for x. $-5x = 140$

10. Simplify. $3\sqrt{2} \cdot 7\sqrt{2}$

11. Solve for x. $\frac{5}{6}x - \frac{4}{6}x + 5 = 14$

12. Simplify. $\sqrt{100a^{12}b^{16}}$

13. Use the quadratic formula to solve. $a^2 + 2a - 3 = 0$

14. Simplify. $3\sqrt{2x^5} \cdot 4\sqrt{8x}$

15. The slope of a horizontal line is _____.

16. Solve for x. $\frac{5}{7} = \frac{x}{105}$

17. Solve for x. $3x - 7 = 14$

18. $29 - 18\frac{5}{8} = ?$

19. Solve for x. $\frac{-3}{5}x = 15$

20. What are the coordinates of points B and C?

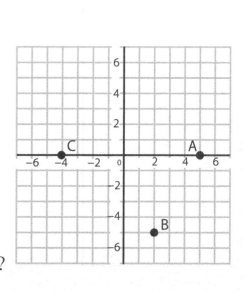

1.	2.	3.	4.
5.	6.	7.	8.
9.	10.	11.	12.
13.	14.	15.	16.
17.	18.	19.	20.

Lesson #11

1. $33 + (-13) + 26 = ?$

2. Write 0.000057 in scientific notation.

3. Find the missing measurement.

4. Write the equation for a line through point (4, 6) with a slope of –5.

5. Factor. $2x^2 + 5x - 3$

6. Find the area of the quadrilateral.

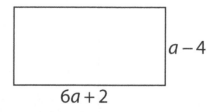

7. Simplify. $\dfrac{\sqrt{45}}{\sqrt{5}}$

8. Simplify. $(6c^4 d^5)^2$

9. $-102 - (-68) = ?$

10. How many feet are in 6 miles?

11. Simplify. $9\sqrt{5} - 4\sqrt{5}$

12. What percent of 80 is 64?

13. Simplify. $\dfrac{(a+3)(a+4)}{(a-3)(a+4)}$

14. Factor out the GCF. $5a^3 - 10a^2 + 15a$

15. Solve the system using any method. $\begin{array}{l} 3x - y = 4 \\ x + 5y = -4 \end{array}$

16. What is the P(H, T, H,) on three flips of a coin?

17. Solve for a. $6a + 7 = -29$

18. Multiply. $(x + 8)(x - 7)$

19. Solve. $5 \cdot 3 + 4 \cdot 2 + 16 \div 4$

20. There are ten marbles in a bag. Four of the marbles are black, three of the marbles are red, two are green, and one is white. What is the P(black, white) with replacement?

1.	2.	3.	4.
5.	6.	7.	8.
9.	10.	11.	12.
13.	14.	15.	16.
17.	18.	19.	20.

Lesson #12

1.   Multiply. $(x + 8)(x - 3)$

2.   Solve for x. $8x - 12 = 5x$

3. $8.624 \div 0.04 = ?$

4.   Simplify. $5n^3 \cdot 4n^5$

5.   Write 0.000031 in scientific notation.

6.   Solve for c. $\frac{1}{3}c = 6$

7.   Factor out the GCF from this expression. $6a^2 - 9a + 15$

8.   Solve for x. $\frac{7}{9}x - \frac{6}{9}x - 5 = 10$

9.   Simplify. $8\sqrt{5} + 5\sqrt{5}$

10.   Find the perimeter of the square.

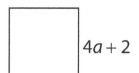

$4a + 2$

11.   Write as an algebraic expression: eight times a number decreased by seven.

12. $-24 + (-18) + (-32) = ?$

13.   Simplify. $\dfrac{2x - 10}{x - 5}$

14.   Two angles whose measures add up to 90° are called _____ angles.

15.   Find the values for y in the equation, $y = -2x + 2$, when $x = \{ 0, -4, 2\}$.

16. $\frac{8}{15} \cdot \frac{12}{16} = ?$

17.   Simplify. $(-4)^{-2}$

18.   Simplify. $(k^{10})^5$

19.   Write $\frac{2}{25}$ as a decimal and as a percent.

20.   Solve the system of equations using any method you choose. $\begin{aligned} x + y &= 12 \\ x - y &= 2 \end{aligned}$

1.	2.	3.	4.
5.	6.	7.	8.
9.	10.	11.	12.
13.	14.	15.	16.
17.	18.	19.	20.

Lesson #13

1. Solve for x. $\frac{5}{6} = \frac{x}{42}$

2. Find $\frac{3}{7}$ of 56.

3. Which is greater, $\frac{8}{25}$ or 36%?

4. $-27 + (-13) + (-41) = ?$

5. Write 3.4×10^4 in standard notation.

6. Multiply. $(7a^2 - 4a + 2)(a + 5)$

7. Simplify. $(5a^3b^2c^4)^2$

8. $56\frac{1}{7} + 43\frac{2}{5} = ?$

9. $-146 - 88 = ?$

10. Find the area of the square.

11. Evaluate. $55 + 14 \div 2 + 3 \cdot 4$

$5x - 3$

12. Solve for t. $5(t + 1) = 10$

13. Simplify. $\dfrac{8ab^{-2}}{2c^{-3}}$

14. Factor the polynomial. $y^2 - 9y + 14$

15. Solve for x. $4x - 9 \geq 15$

16. Simplify. $\sqrt{81b^6c^8}$

17. Simplify. $4\sqrt{3} - \sqrt{12}$

18. Write an algebraic phrase for the quotient of a number and eleven decreased by four.

19. Find the quotient. $\dfrac{x}{x+4} \div \dfrac{x+3}{x+4}$

20. Find the difference. $\begin{array}{r} 13a^3 - 6a^2 \quad\quad + 7 \\ -\ 6a^3 + 2a^2 - 2a - 3 \\ \hline \end{array}$

1.	2.	3.	4.
5.	6.	7.	8.
9.	10.	11.	12.
13.	14.	15.	16.
17.	18.	19.	20.

Lesson #14

1. $-85 + (-63) = ?$

2. Simplify. $(6x^2y^4)^3$

3. The slope of a horizontal line is _____.

4. Factor out the GCF. $10x^2 - 5x + 5$

5. Find the quotient. $\dfrac{3t+12}{5t} \div \dfrac{t+4}{10t}$

6. Multiply. $(5a + 3)(3a + 6)$

7. Simplify. $10^{-2}a^3b^{-4}c$

8. Write the formula for finding the circumference of a circle.

9. Factor. $d^2 - 7d + 12$

10. Find the missing measurement.

11. A triangle with all sides congruent is called a(n) _____ triangle.

12. How many feet are in 7 miles?

13. Find the area of a triangle if the base is 24 meters and the height is 8 meters.

14. Simplify. $\sqrt{\dfrac{4}{36}}$

15. What is the P(H, T, H, T, H, T) on six flips of a coin?

16. On the Fahrenheit temperature scale, water boils at _____.

17. $46.5 \times 0.3 = ?$

18. Write 0.000628 in scientific notation.

19. $\sqrt{400} = ?$

20. The perimeter of this triangle is $(23a - 7)$. Find the length of the third side.

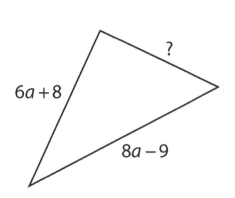

1.	2.	3.	4.
5.	6.	7.	8.
9.	10.	11.	12.
13.	14.	15.	16.
17.	18.	19.	20.

Lesson #15

1. Simplify. $\dfrac{24y + 18}{36}$

2. $79 - (-48) = ?$

3. Find the area of the square.

$4x - 3$

4. Simplify. $5^{-3}a^2b^{-4}c$

5. Multiply the rational expression. $\dfrac{6x^4}{5y^7} \cdot \dfrac{3y^5}{8x}$

6. Write the slope-intercept form of a linear equation.

7. Multiply. $(3x - 2)(x + 3)$

8. $0.71 - 0.4629 = ?$

9. Write 6.13×10^5 in standard notation.

10. Factor. $9y^2 - 25$

11. Which is greater, $\dfrac{3}{50}$ or 15%?

12. Factor out the GCF. $12b^3 - 18b^2 + 24$

13. Simplify. $(5c^2d^3f^4)^2$

14. Solve for x. $x + 9 = 2x - 6$

15. Solve for p. $p - 52 = 106$

16. Evaluate the expression $abc + ab$
    if $a = 2$, $b = 5$, and $c = 5$.

17. Simplify. $4x(2x^2)(3x^3)$

18. $30 \div 5 + 6 \cdot 3 - 10 + 5 = ?$

19. Simplify. $10\sqrt{3} - 6\sqrt{3}$

20. Solve for x. $\frac{x}{7} + 5 = 13$

1.	2.	3.	4.
5.	6.	7.	8.
9.	10.	11.	12.
13.	14.	15.	16.
17.	18.	19.	20.

Lesson #16

1. Solve for x. $5x - 9 = 36$

2. Simplify. $-\sqrt{16x^8 y^{12}}$

3. Multiply. $(x + 6)(x - 3)$

4. Write 0.0000072 in scientific notation.

5. Find the slope of a line passing through points (0, 4) and (2, 2).

6. $157 - (-79) = ?$

7. Simplify. $\sqrt{50}$

8. Multiply. $\dfrac{x^2 + 13x + 42}{x^2 - 3x - 40} \cdot \dfrac{x - 8}{x + 6}$

9. Factor. $a^2 - 9a + 14$

10. Simplify. $3\sqrt{16y^3}$

11. Multiply. $4d(3d^2 - 5d)$

12. Divide. $\dfrac{m^2}{p^2} \div \dfrac{p^4}{m^4}$

13. Simplify. $\sqrt{\dfrac{25}{64}}$

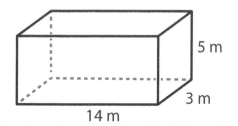

14. Find the surface area of the rectangular prism.

15. Simplify. $a \cdot a^{-6}$

16. 80% of what number is 64?

17. Write the formula for finding the area of a circle.

18. Solve the system using any method you choose. $x - y = 12$
    $x + y = 22$

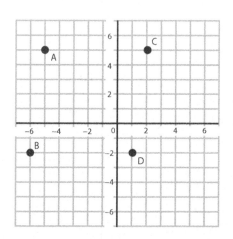

19. Solve for m. $-6m = -90$

20. Give the coordinates of points A and C.

1.	2.	3.	4.
5.	6.	7.	8.
9.	10.	11.	12.
13.	14.	15.	16.
17.	18.	19.	20.

Lesson #17

1. Factor. $y^2 - 16y + 64$

2. $-5(-8)(2) = ?$

3. Multiply. $(5a^3 - 2a^2 + 4)(a - 3)$

4. Solve for x. $\frac{3}{8} = \frac{x}{96}$

5. Find the area of the parallelogram.

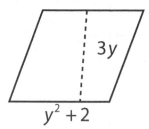

6. $244 + (-87) = ?$

7. Simplify. $3\sqrt{18a^{17}b^{15}}$

8. Write an algebraic phrase for three times a number increased by seven.

9. $30 - 3 \cdot 5 + 8 \div 2 - 1 = ?$

10. Multiply the rational expression. $\dfrac{x^2 + 7x + 12}{x + 5} \cdot \dfrac{5x + 25}{x + 4}$

11. Solve for x. $\frac{8}{9}x - \frac{7}{9}x + 6 = 13$

12. Jasmine bought a guitar for $900. If the sales tax was 7%, what was the total cost of the guitar?

13. Solve for y. $|y - 3| = 7$

14. Simplify. $(x^{-8}y^{-5})(x^{10}y^{-2})$

15. Find the LCM of $12x^3y^2z^4$ and $15x^2yz^2$.

16. 90% of what number is 81?

17. Factor out the GCF. $5x - 25$

18. Solve for m. $14 - 9m = -11m$

19. Write 91,000,000 in scientific notation.

20. Find the sum. $\begin{aligned} 17x^2 - 6x + 1 \\ +\ 8x^2\qquad -5 \end{aligned}$

1.	2.	3.	4.
5.	6.	7.	8.
9.	10.	11.	12.
13.	14.	15.	16.
17.	18.	19.	20.

Lesson #18

1. Simplify. $(d^3)^{-7}$

2. Multiply. $(6x - 3)(x + 4)$

3. Solve for x. $\frac{x}{9} + 3 = 10$

4. Factor. $y^2 + 9y + 14$

5. Write an algebraic phrase for the sum of a number and five.

6. Simplify. $\dfrac{3x^3 - 12x}{6x^4 - 12x^3}$

7. $-243 + (-129) = ?$

8. Solve for c. $c + 17 = -51$

9. Evaluate $\dfrac{ab}{4} + 2b$ if $a = 3$ and $b = 8$.

10. Use the quadratic equation to solve. $(x + 4)(3x - 15) = 0$

11. Simplify. $a^{-4}b^2cd^{-3}$

12. Find the perimeter of the triangle.

    $4a + 1$ $4a + 1$

    $2a - 1$

13. Solve for b. $-6b = 96$

14. Solve for x. $4x + 2x - 6 = 30$

15. Find $\frac{3}{8}$ of 120.

16. Write 8.17×10^{-4} in standard form.

17. Find the percent of change from 14 hours to 24 hours. Round your answer to the nearest percent.

18. Graph the solution on a number line. $3a - 4 > 8$

19. Write $\frac{3}{50}$ as a decimal and a percent.

20. The ratio of basketballs to footballs in the gym store room is 5 to 7. If there are 105 footballs, how many basketballs are in the store room?

1.	2.	3.	4.
5.	6.	7.	8.
9.	10.	11.	12.
13.	14.	15.	16.
17.	18.	19.	20.

Lesson #19

1.   Find the slope of a line passing through points (0, 5) and (4, 9).

2.   Solve for x. $\frac{x}{9} = 17$

3.   Write an algebraic phrase to represent the quotient of a number and five decreased by six.

4. $\frac{-344}{-4} = ?$

5.   Simplify. $\frac{(5x-3)(x+9)}{(x+1)(5x-3)}$

6. $\left|-46\right| = ?$

7.   Factor. $c^2 - c - 56$

8.   Multiply. $\frac{6}{10x} \cdot \frac{5}{2}$

9.   Multiply. $(8x^2 + 4x - 3)(2x - 2)$

10.   Factor out the GCF. $36a^3 + 12a^2 - 24a$

11. $4.6 + 22.78 + 9.329 = ?$

12.   Put these in increasing order. $0.56, \frac{3}{5}, 38\%$

13.   Find the volume of the cylinder.

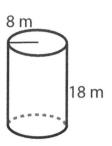

8 m

18 m

14.   Write 35,000,000,000 in scientific notation.

15.   The boiling temperature of water is _____°C.

16.   Solve for a. $25 - 5a = 6a + 3$

17.   Simplify. $\sqrt{63m^7n^5}$

18. $-21 \bigcirc -64$

19. $21\frac{2}{5} + 17\frac{2}{3} = ?$

20.   Simplify. $\frac{\sqrt{50x^3}}{\sqrt{2x}}$

1.	2.	3.	4.
5.	6.	7.	8.
9.	10.	11.	12.
13.	14.	15.	16.
17.	18.	19.	20.

Lesson #20

1. $\frac{8}{12} \div \frac{3}{4} = ?$

2.   Simplify. $3\sqrt{20x^{13}}$

3.   Factor. $4a^2 - 11a - 3$

4. $0.008 \times 0.004 = ?$

5.   Simplify. $\dfrac{8a^3b^2c}{10abc}$

6.   Multiply. $(x + 8)(x + 5)$

7. $\sqrt{196} = ?$

8.   Simplify. $(x^3y^4z^2)^4$

9. $-5(9)(-2) = ?$

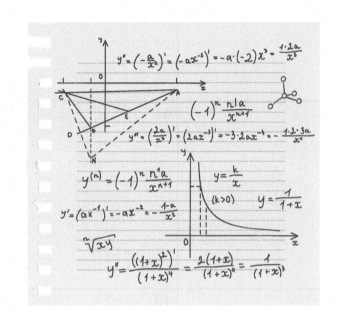

10.   Simplify. $(3a^3)(4a^2)(2a)$

11.   Solve the inequality. $-2y \le 24$

12.   Find the perimeter of the regular pentagon.

$2a + 2$

13.   Find the GCF of $9a^3b^2c^3$ and $12a^2b^2c^2$.

14.   Simplify. $7^0x^2y^{-3}$

15.   What is the P(H, H, H, H, T) on five flips of a coin?

16.   Solve for y. $|y - 6| = 10$

17.   Find the value of x. $\frac{3}{5}x = 75$

18.   Find the circumference of a circle if the diameter is 18 inches.

19.   Solve for x. $\frac{2}{9} = \frac{x}{117}$

20.   Multiply. $\dfrac{6x^2}{2x - 4} \cdot \dfrac{x - 2}{1}$

1.	2.	3.	4.
5.	6.	7.	8.
9.	10.	11.	12.
13.	14.	15.	16.
17.	18.	19.	20.

Lesson #21

1. Solve the inequality. $-4 < 7 + x < 2$

2. $175 + (-79) = ?$

3. Solve for y. $|y - 3| < 7$

4a + 6

4. Determine the area of the square.

5. Multiply. $(4x + 5)(2x - 3)$

6. Write 9.16×10^7 in standard notation.

7. Find the difference. $(15x^3 - 8x^2 + 8x - 9) - (7x^3 + 3x^2 - 3x + 1)$

8. Multiply. $3d(3d^3 - 5d^2 + 7)$

9. Write the slope-intercept form of a linear equation.

10. A triangle in which no two sides have the same length is a(n) _____ triangle.

11. Factor. $s^2 - 11s + 28$

12. Simplify. $6x^4 y^{-5} z^{-3}$

13. Simplify. $8\sqrt{45x^{32}}$

14. $0.44 - 0.1638 = ?$

15. Solve for x. $x - 16 = -22$

16. Evaluate the expression, $rst - s$, if $r = 5$, $s = 3$, and $t = 4$.

17. Find $\frac{4}{9}$ of 81.

18. Solve for x. $\frac{x}{7} - 9 = 4$

19. What is the mean of 25, 35, and 75?

20. Simplify. $\frac{10}{3b} - \frac{6}{3b}$

1.	2.	3.	4.
5.	6.	7.	8.
9.	10.	11.	12.
13.	14.	15.	16.
17.	18.	19.	20.

Lesson #22

1.   Multiply. $(6a^2 + 2a + 3)(a + 4)$

2.   How many grams are in 16 kilograms?

3.   Write 99,000 in scientific notation.

4.   Solve for y. $-5y = 85$

5.   Find the area of the trapezoid.

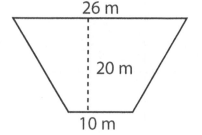

6.   Write an algebraic phrase that means six less than five times a number.

7.   Simplify. $2^{-3}x^4z^3$

8. $-53 + (-27) + 20 = ?$

9.   Factor. $c^2 - 49$

10.   Simplify. $(f^5)^5$

11. $36 \div 9 + 3 \cdot 5 - 4 \cdot 1 = ?$

12.   Simplify. $2\sqrt{63c^5}$

13.   Solve for h. $h + 44 = -81$

14.   Factor out the GCF. $8b^3 - 16b^2 + 24b$

15.   Find the percent of change from 8 yards to 12 yards.

16.   Multiply. $\dfrac{12(a-2)}{a-4} \cdot \dfrac{a-4}{6(a+5)}$

17.   Find the values for y in the equation, $y = 2x + 1$, when $x = \{0, -5, 3\}$.

18.   Give the formula for finding the volume of a cube.

19.   Write $\frac{7}{20}$ as a decimal and a percent.

20.   Solve for x. $4x + 2x - 9 = 45$

1.	2.	3.	4.
5.	6.	7.	8.
9.	10.	11.	12.
13.	14.	15.	16.
17.	18.	19.	20.

Lesson #23

1.   Solve for x. $6x - 6 = 3x$

2.   Simplify. $5ab^3(a^2b^4)$

3. $-121 + (-57) = ?$

4.   Find the product. $(4x^2 - 3x + 2)(x - 2)$

5.   Write the slope and the y-intercept of the line whose equation is $y = 7x - 3$.

6. $\frac{-96}{-4} = ?$

7.   Factor. $x^2 - 16x + 48$

8.   Simplify. $6\sqrt{45a^{15}b^9}$

9.   What is the formula for finding the area of a circle?

10.   Write 7.5×10^{-6} in standard notation.

11.   Multiply. $5a(4a^2 + 6a - 7)$

12.   Add. $\frac{7x}{3} + \frac{2x}{3}$

13. $\begin{pmatrix} 6 & -3 & 4 \\ 5 & -1 & 1 \end{pmatrix} + \begin{pmatrix} 3 & -2 & -9 \\ 0 & 5 & -7 \end{pmatrix} = ?$

14.   80% of 35 is what number?

15. $45 + 3[4 + 2(5) - 2] = ?$

16.   Solve for x. $\frac{x}{8} = 14$

17.   Solve for x. $2x + 3(x - 2) = 24$

18.   Divide. $\frac{x^2}{3y} \div \frac{6x}{4y^3}$

19.   What is the sum? $\frac{5b}{21} + \frac{2b}{21} + \frac{8b}{21}$

$8a + 3$

20.   Find the perimeter of the square.

46

1.	2.	3.	4.
5.	6.	7.	8.
9.	10.	11.	12.
13.	14.	15.	16.
17.	18.	19.	20.

Lesson #24

1.   Solve for x. $7x - 6 = 22$

2.   Simplify. $(d^4)^{-3}$

3. $-88 + (-39) = ?$

4.   Solve for x. $\frac{3}{2} = \frac{27}{x}$

5.   Evaluate $5a - 2b + ab$, if $a = 4$ and $b = 3$.

6.   Factor. $t^2 - 6t + 9$

7.   Multiply. $7m(3m - 5)$

8.   Write the equation of a line through $(3, -1)$ with a slope of 1.

9.   What value of h will make this true? $4h + 5 = 9h$

10.   Write 740,000,000,000 in scientific notation.

11.   Solve using any method you choose. $\begin{aligned} x + y &= 19 \\ x - y &= -7 \end{aligned}$

12.   A jar has five blue, three yellow, six green, and two red balls. You pick two balls from the jar. What is the P(R, B) with replacement? What is the P(Y, G) without replacement?

13.   Simplify. $(5x^3)(4x)(2x^2)$

14.   Find the percent of change from 18 miles to 20 miles. Round your answer.

15.   What is the solution to this inequality? $37 < 3c + 7 < 43$

16.   Factor out the GCF. $5r + 15r^3 + 25r^2$

17.   Write the quadratic formula.

18.   Multiply. $(3a - 1)(2a + 1)$

19.   Find the perimeter of the rectangle.

20.   Simplify. $\dfrac{16 - y^2}{y^2 - 5y + 4}$

1.	2.	3.	4.
5.	6.	7.	8.
9.	10.	11.	12.
13.	14.	15.	16.
17.	18.	19.	20.

Lesson #25

1. $-11(-3)(-2) = ?$

2. Find the slope of a line passing through points (1, 3) and (5, 6).

3. Multiply. $(6s^2 + 3s - 4)(2s + 2)$

4. Factor. $x^2 + 7x + 12$

5. Solve for x. $\frac{x}{10} - 5 = 9$

6. Find the area of the triangle.

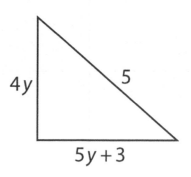

7. Write 0.00000662 in scientific notation.

8. Simplify. $(2x^3)(5x^2)(4x)$

9. Multiply. $8c^2(2c^2 + 3c - 5)$

10. How many cups are in 18 pints?

11. Solve for x. $\frac{4}{6}x = -24$

12. Simplify. $(7a^5b^3c^2)^2$

13. Write $\frac{9}{25}$ as a decimal and as a percent.

14. Solve for x. $5x + 3 = 2x + 6$

15. Simplify. $4\sqrt{36x^{12}y^8}$

16. Find the LCM of $10a^3b^2$ and $16a^2bc^2$.

17. Multiply. $\dfrac{9y^2}{4 - 2y} \cdot \dfrac{5y - 10}{21y}$

18. Simplify. $3\sqrt{7} + 8\sqrt{7}$

19. $63\frac{2}{9} + 38\frac{1}{5} = ?$

20. Simplify. $\dfrac{6x}{x - 3} - \dfrac{3x}{x - 3}$

1.	2.	3.	4.
5.	6.	7.	8.
9.	10.	11.	12.
13.	14.	15.	16.
17.	18.	19.	20.

Lesson #26

1. Put these integers in increasing order. $-31, -16, 0, -5, -29$

2. Solve for h. $|h - 4| = 11$

3. Graph the solution on a number line. $2x + 3 \le 9$

4. $144 + (-98) = ?$

5. Simplify. $\dfrac{3p - 18}{2p - 12}$

6. $18 \div 3 + 3 \cdot 5 - 12 \div 6 = ?$

7. Write eight less than a number using an algebraic phrase.

8. Write 1.7×10^9 in standard notation.

9. $18 - 7\frac{5}{7} = ?$

10. Factor. $a^2 - 64$

11. Solve for c. $7c - 9 = 8c$

12. Multiply. $(3x + 2)(2x - 1)$

13. Simplify. $-4\sqrt{25x^9}$

14. $6.23 \times 0.6 = ?$

15. Find the sum of $(13a^2 - 7)$ and $(5a^2 + 3)$.

16. Simplify. $\dfrac{10c^2 d}{16cd^3}$

17. Solve using any system. $\begin{array}{l} 3x + 7y = 3 \\ x - 7y = 1 \end{array}$

18. $\frac{7}{9} \times \frac{18}{21} = ?$

19. Find the volume of the cube.

20. Subtract. $\dfrac{5a + 4}{9a} - \dfrac{3a - 1}{12a}$

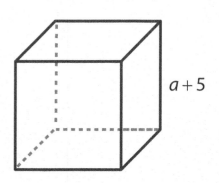

$a + 5$

1.	2.	3.	4.
5.	6.	7.	8.
9.	10.	11.	12.
13.	14.	15.	16.
17.	18.	19.	20.

Lesson #27

1. Solve for x. $3x - 7 = 14$

2. Multiply. $(x - 9)(x + 4)$

3. Factor. $y^2 - 10y + 16$

4. Simplify. $12\sqrt{16} - \sqrt{16}$

5. Solve for y. $2(y + 4) = 16$

6. Simplify. $\dfrac{(8x^2)(2x^4)}{2x}$

7. The slope of a horizontal line is _____.

8. Simplify. $3^2 c^{-2} d^3$

9. $-\left|-33\right| = ?$

10. Write the Pythagorean Theorem.

11. Simplify. $\sqrt{x^9 y^7}$

12. Use the Pythagorean Theorem to find the hypotenuse, C.

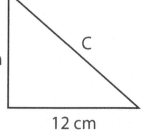

9 cm   C   12 cm

13. What percent of 80 is 72?

14. Find the percent of change from 15 inches to 25 inches.

15. What is the term given to the side opposite the right angle in a right triangle?

16. Write 623,000,000 in scientific notation.

17. Simplify. $\sqrt{27}$

18. Multiply. $6p(6p^2 - 5p + 2)$

19. Find the difference. $(21x^3 + 18x^2 + 7) - (11x^3 + 10x^2 - 5)$

20. Add. $\dfrac{a-4}{3a-2} + \dfrac{a+3}{1}$

1.	2.	3.	4.
5.	6.	7.	8.
9.	10.	11.	12.
13.	14.	15.	16.
17.	18.	19.	20.

Lesson #28

1. Simplify. $(t^{10})^{-4}$

2. Write the Pythagorean Theorem.

3. $14\frac{2}{7} - 9\frac{6}{7} = ?$

4. Solve for x. $\frac{3}{5} = \frac{x}{60}$

5. Write 3.2×10^{-3} in standard notation.

6. $56.2 + 8.219 = ?$

7. Simplify. $\dfrac{\left(4a^3\right)\left(5a^2\right)}{2a}$

8. Factor. $x^2 - 8x + 16$

9. Which is greater, $\frac{9}{25}$ or 0.40?

10. Find the area of the parallelogram.

11. Simplify. $3\sqrt{16a^5b^2c^7}$

12. Multiply. $(5x + 3)(3x - 2)$

13. Find the missing measurement.

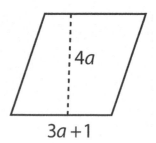

14. Simplify. $\dfrac{8a^3 - 4a^4}{5a^3 - 10a^2}$

15. Find the length of the hypotenuse.

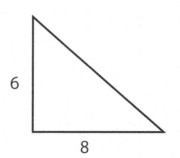

16. Solve for a. $|a + 5| = 4$

17. Subtract. $\dfrac{a+2}{1} - \dfrac{a}{a+1}$

18. Write an equation of a line passing through point (4, 0) with a slope of 7.

19. Find the values for y in the equation, $y = -4x + 1$, when $x = \{-2, 4, -3\}$.

20. Solve for x. $\frac{x}{9} - 5 = 6$

1.	2.	3.	4.
5.	6.	7.	8.
9.	10.	11.	12.
13.	14.	15.	16.
17.	18.	19.	20.

Lesson #29

1. Find the coordinates of points B and D.

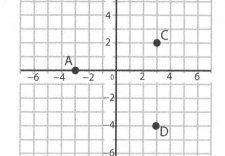

2. $-25(-3) = ?$

3. The slope of a vertical line is _____.

4. Write the Pythagorean Theorem.

5. Factor. $2c^2 - 5c - 3$

6. Divide. $\dfrac{3x^3}{2} \div \dfrac{-15x^5}{1}$

7. Multiply. $(6b^2 - 4b + 2)(2b + 4)$

8. Simplify. $\dfrac{4^{-2}x^{-3}y^2}{x^2y}$

9. How many feet are in 7 miles?

10. Multiply. $\dfrac{5x^3}{x^2} \cdot \dfrac{3x^4}{10x}$

11. Find the area of the rectangle.

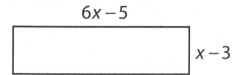

12. Simplify. $5\sqrt{18x^4y^8}$

13. Solve for x. $x - 33 = -72$

14. Subtract. $\dfrac{a}{2} - \dfrac{3a}{10}$

15. The perimeter of the rectangle is $(38y + 2)$. Find its width.

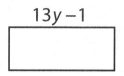

16. Write 0.0049 in scientific notation.

17. $16\frac{1}{8} + 27\frac{2}{5} = ?$

18. Solve for x. $7 - 3x > 4x - 21$

19. Find the length of the missing side.

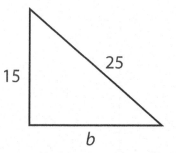

20. $-56 - (-22) = ?$

1.	2.	3.	4.
5.	6.	7.	8.
9.	10.	11.	12.
13.	14.	15.	16.
17.	18.	19.	20.

Lesson #30

1.   Find the solution. $5x - 8 \geq 7$

2.   Write the slope-intercept form for a linear equation.

3.   Simplify. $(5x^2y)(-6xy^2)$

4.   Multiply. $(x + 7)(x + 4)$

5.   Write the Pythagorean Theorem.

6. $-51 - (-28) = ?$

7.   Multiply. $\dfrac{3x^7}{4y^5} \cdot \dfrac{2y^6}{3x^8}$

8.   Simplify. $(3b^3c^2d^4)^4$

9.   Simplify. $5\sqrt{20a^5b^{11}}$

10.   Add. $\dfrac{3x - 5}{4} + \dfrac{5x - 3}{3}$

11.   Translate fourteen times a number divided by two into an algebraic phrase.

12.   What is the P(1, 4, 2) on 3 rolls of a die?

13.   Factor out the GCF. $8x^4 - 12x^3 + 20x^2$

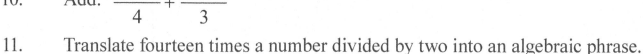

14.   Find the area of the square.

15.   Evaluate $cd - c$ if $c = 12$ and $d = 3$.

16. $20 - 4[3 + 2(3 + 2) - 3] = ?$

17.   Write 5.3×10^6 in standard notation.

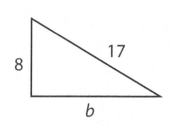

18.   Find the missing length of the leg.

19.   Factor. $x^2 - 15x + 56$

20.   Find the difference. $\begin{array}{r} 0.8x^2 + 0.5x - 0.9 \\ - \;\; 0.2x^2 + 0.2x + 0.5 \\ \hline \end{array}$

1.	2.	3.	4.
5.	6.	7.	8.
9.	10.	11.	12.
13.	14.	15.	16.
17.	18.	19.	20.

Algebra I

Part B

Mathematics

3rd Edition

Help Pages

Help Pages

Vocabulary

General
absolute value — the distance between a number, x, and zero on a number line; written as $\|x\|$. Example: $\|5\| = 5$ reads, "The absolute value of 5 is 5." $\|-7\| = 7$ reads, "The absolute value of -7 is 7."
binomial — a polynomial having exactly 2 terms. Examples: $3x - 7$, $2x + 5y$, $2y^2 + x^3$
complementary angles — two angles whose measures add up to 90°.
expression — a mathematical phrase written in symbols. Example: $2x + 5$ is an expression.
function — a rule that pairs each number in a given set (the domain) with just one number in another set (the range). Example: The function $y = x + 3$ pairs every number with another number that is larger by 3.
hypotenuse — in a right triangle, the side opposite the right angle. 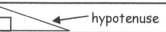
integers — the set of whole numbers, positive or negative, and zero.
irrational number — a number that cannot be written as the ratio of two whole numbers. The decimal form of an irrational number is neither terminating nor repeating. Examples: $\sqrt{2}$ and π.
legs — in a right triangle, the sides adjacent to the right angle. The two legs actually form the right angle. 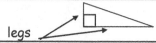
matrix — a rectangular arrangement of numbers in rows and columns. Each number in a matrix is an element or entry. The plural of matrix is matrices. Example: $\begin{pmatrix} 2 & 3 \\ 0 & -1 \end{pmatrix}$ is a matrix with 4 elements.
monomial — a number, a variable, or the product of numbers and variables with or without exponents. Examples: $3x$, 7, $2xy$, $2y^2$, x^3
polynomial — a monomial or the sum of monomials. Each monomial is called a term of the polynomial. Example: $3x^2 - 7 + 2x + 5y - 2y^2 + x^3$
Pythagorean Theorem — a statement of the relationship between the lengths of the sides in a right triangle. If a and b are legs, and c is the hypotenuse, $a^2 + b^2 = c^2$.
quadratic equation — a polynomial in the form of $ax^2 + bx + c$, where $a \neq 0$.
radical expression — an expression that contains a radical, such as a square root or cubed root.
rational number — a number that can be written as the ratio of two whole numbers. Example: 7 is rational; it can be written as $\frac{7}{1}$. 0.25 is rational; it can be written as $\frac{1}{4}$.
slope — the ratio of the *rise* (vertical change) to the *run* (horizontal change) for a non-vertical line.
square root — a number that when multiplied by itself is another number. The symbol for square root is $\sqrt{x}$. Example: $\sqrt{49} = 7$ reads, "The square root of 49 is 7."
straight angle — an angle measuring exactly 180°.
supplementary angles — two angles whose measures add up to 180°. 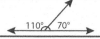
surface area — the sum of the areas of all of the faces of a solid figure.
term — the components of an expression, usually being added to or subtracted from each other. Example: The expression $2x + 5$ has two terms: $2x$ and 5. The expression $3n^2$ has only one term.
trinomial — a polynomial having exactly 3 terms. Examples: $3x^2 - 7 + 2x$, $5y + 2y^2 - x^3$

Help Pages

Vocabulary (continued)

Geometry — Circles

circumference — the distance around the outside of a circle.

diameter — the widest distance across a circle. The diameter always passes through the center.

radius — the distance from any point on the circle to the center. The radius is half of the diameter.

Geometry — Polygons

Number of Sides		Name	Number of Sides		Name
3	△	triangle	7	⬡	heptagon
4	☐	quadrilateral	8	⬡	octagon
5	⬠	pentagon	9	⬡	nonagon
6	⬡	hexagon	10	⬡	decagon

Geometry — Triangles

equilateral — a triangle in which all 3 sides have the same length.

isosceles — a triangle in which 2 sides have the same length.

scalene — a triangle in which no sides are the same length.

Measurement — Relationships

Volume	Distance
3 teaspoons in a tablespoon	36 inches in a yard
2 cups in a pint	1,760 yards in a mile
2 pints in a quart	5,280 feet in a mile
4 quarts in a gallon	100 centimeters in a meter
Weight	1,000 millimeters in a meter
16 ounces in a pound	**Temperature**
2,000 pounds in a ton	0°Celsius – freezing point
Time	100°Celsius – boiling point
10 years in a decade	32°Fahrenheit – freezing point
100 years in a century	212°Fahrenheit – boiling point

Help Pages

Solved Examples

Absolute Value

The **absolute value** of a number is its distance from zero on a number line. It is always positive.

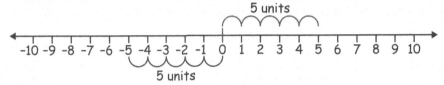

5 units

The absolute value of both -5 and +5 is 5, because both are 5 units away from zero. The symbol for the absolute value of -5 is |-5|. Examples: |-3| = 3; |8| = 8

Equations

More complicated equations involve variables which replace a number. To solve an equation like this, you must figure out which number the variable stands for. There is a process for solving for the variable. No matter how complicated the equation, <u>the goal is to work with the equation until all the numbers are on one side and the variable is alone on the other side</u>. To check the answer, put the value of x back into the original equation.

These multi-step equations also have a variable on only one side. To get the variable alone, though, requires several steps.

Example: Solve for x.

$$3(2x + 3) = 21$$

$$\cancel{3}\left(\frac{2x + 3}{\cancel{3}}\right) = \frac{21}{3}$$

$$2x + 3 = 7$$
$$\underline{-3 = -3}$$
$$2x \quad = 4$$

$$\frac{\cancel{2}x}{\cancel{2}} = \frac{4}{2}$$

$$x = 2$$

1. Look at the side of the equation that has the variable on it. First, the expression $(2x + 3)$ is multiplied by 3; then there is a number (3) added to $2x$, and there is a number (2) multiplied by x. All of these must be removed. To remove the 3 outside the parentheses, divide both sides by 3. Divide because it is the opposite operation from the one in the equation (multiplication).
2. To remove the 3 inside the parentheses, add its opposite (-3) to both sides.
3. Remove the 2 by dividing both sides by 2.
4. Follow the rules for multiplying or dividing integers. $2x$ divided by 2 is x. 4 divided by 2 is 2.
5. Once the variable is alone on one side of the equation, the equation is solved. The bottom line tells the value of x. $x = 2$.

Check: $3\big(2(2) + 3\big) = 21$

$$3(4 + 3) = 21$$

$$3(7) = 21$$

$$21 = 21 \checkmark \quad \text{correct!}$$

When solving an **equation with a variable on both sides**, the goals are the same: to get the numbers on one side of the equation and to get the variable alone on the other side.

Example: Solve for x. $2x + 4 = 6x - 4$

$$2x + 4 = 6x - 4$$
$$\underline{-2x \quad\;\; = -2x}$$
$$4 = 4x - 4$$
$$\underline{+4 = \qquad +4}$$
$$8 = 4x$$

$$\frac{8}{4} = \frac{\cancel{4}x}{\cancel{4}}$$

$$2 = x$$

1. Since there are variables on both sides, the first step is to remove the "variable term" from one of the sides. To remove $2x$ from the left side, add $-2x$ to both sides.

2. Next, remove the number added to the variable side by adding its opposite. To remove -4, add +4 to both sides.

3. The variable still has a number multiplied by it (4), which can be removed by dividing both sides by 4.

Help Pages

Solved Examples

Equations (continued)

A **quadratic equation** is a polynomial in the form $ax^2 + bx + c = 0$ where $a \neq 0$. Some quadratic equations can be solved simply by factoring and then setting them equal to zero.

Example: Solve the equation for x. $x^2 + 5x + 6 = 0$

$$x^2 + 5x + 6 = (x+2)(x+3)$$

$$(x+2)(x+3) = 0$$

$$(x+2) = 0, \quad x = -2$$

$$(x+3) = 0, \quad x = -3$$

$$x = \{-2, -3\}$$

1. First, factor the quadratic.
2. Next, substitute the factors into the equation.
3. To solve for x, realize that one or both of the factors must equal zero.
4. The values of x that make the factors equal zero are the solutions.

Sometimes a quadratic equation can't be factored. In that case, the method described above is not useful; in this case, the **quadratic formula** must be used.

For quadratic equations in the standard form $ax^2 + bx + c = 0$,

the quadratic formula is $x = \dfrac{-b \pm \sqrt{b^2 - 4ac}}{2a}$, where $a \neq 0$ and $b^2 - 4ac \geq 0$.

Example: Solve for x. $3x^2 + 5x = 8$

$$3x^2 + 5x = 8$$

$$3x^2 + 5x - 8 = 0$$

$$ax^2 + bx + c = 0$$

$$a = 3, \quad b = 5, \quad c = -8$$

$$x = \frac{-b \pm \sqrt{b^2 - 4ac}}{2a}$$

$$x = \frac{-5 \pm \sqrt{5^2 - 4(3)(-8)}}{2(3)}$$

$$x = \frac{-5 \pm \sqrt{121}}{6}$$

$$x = \frac{-5 + 11}{6} \text{ and } \frac{-5 - 11}{6}$$

$$x = \frac{6}{6} = 1 \text{ and } \frac{-16}{6} = -\frac{8}{3}$$

1. Rewrite the equation in standard form. Remember, in standard form, it must equal 0.
2. Identify the values of a, b, c in the equation.
3. Put the values of a, b, c into the quadratic formula.
4. Simplify each part of the fraction.
5. Because of the $\pm$ in the formula, there will be two solutions.

Example: Solve for n. $n^2 - 7n + 10 = 0$ $\qquad a = 1, \quad b = -7, \quad c = 10$

$$x = \frac{-(-7) \pm \sqrt{(-7)^2 - 4(1)(10)}}{2(1)}$$

$$x = \frac{+7 \pm \sqrt{49 - 40}}{2}$$

$$x = \frac{7 \pm \sqrt{9}}{2}$$

$$x = \frac{7 \pm 3}{2}$$

$$x = \frac{7+3}{2} = \frac{10}{2} = 5$$

$$x = \frac{7-3}{2} = \frac{4}{2} = 2$$

The solutions are 5 and 2.

Help Pages

Solved Examples

Equations (continued)

When solving any equation, there can only be <u>one</u> unknown variable. Sometimes there are multiple variables that are not known. When this is the case, the only way to solve is to use a **system of equations**. A system of equations is a group of equations, all having the same unknown variables. There must be the same number of equations as there are unknown variables. For example, if there are 2 unknown variables, the system must include 2 equations; if there are 3 unknown variables, the system must include 3 equations.

We will use 2 different methods for solving systems of equations: Substitution and Elimination.

To **solve a system of equations by substitution**, there are 3 simple steps:

1. First choose one of the equations, and use it to solve for one of the variables. (Usually this variable will be equal to an expression in terms of the other variable.)

2. Use the expression from step 1 and replace that first variable in the second equation. Solve the second equation for the other variable.

3. Substitute the value from step 2 into the first equation and solve. The values of both variables are known.

Example: Use substitution to solve the system for x and y.

$$y - 2 = 3x \quad \text{Equation 1}$$
$$x + 2y = 11 \quad \text{Equation 2}$$

1. Using Equation 1, solve for y. (This expression is now equal to y.)

2. Using Equation 2, substitute this expression in place of y. Now the equation only has one variable left, x. Solve for x.

3. Now that the value of x is known, go back to Equation 1 and substitute the value of x into the equation. Solve for y.

$$y - 2 = 3x \quad \text{Equation 1}$$
$$y = 3x + 2$$

$$x + 2y = 11 \quad \text{Equation 2}$$
$$x + 2(3x + 2) = 11$$
$$x + 6x + 4 = 11$$
$$7x + 4 = 11$$
$$7x = 7$$
$$x = 1$$

$$y - 2 = 3(1) \quad \text{Equation 1}$$
$$y = 3 + 2$$
$$y = 3 + 2 = 5$$

The solution to this system is $x = 1$ and $y = 5$.

To **solve a system of equations by elimination**, there are also 3 simple steps:

1. Add or subtract the equations to eliminate one of the variables.

2. Solve the resulting equation for the remaining variable.

3. Substitute the value back into either equation. Solve for the value of the eliminated variable.

Example: Use elimination to solve the system for x and y.

$$2x + 3y = 11 \quad \text{Equation 1}$$
$$4x - 3y = 13 \quad \text{Equation 2}$$

1. Add the equations to eliminate one variable, y.

2. Solve for the other variable, x.

3. Substitute the value of x into one of the original equations and solve for y.

$$2x + 3y = 11$$
$$+ \ 4x - 3y = 13$$
$$\overline{\quad 6x \quad = 24}$$
$$x \quad = 4$$

$$2x + 3y = 11$$
$$2(4) + 3y = 11$$
$$8 + 3y = 11$$
$$3y = 3$$
$$y = 1$$

The solution to this system is $x = 4$ and $y = 1$.

Help Pages

Solved Examples

Exponents

Until now, exponents have been positive numbers. What if the exponent is zero or a negative number? The rules for dealing with **negative or zero exponents** are as follows:

a to the zero power is 1. $a^0 = 1, a \neq 0$,   so $7^0 = 1$

a^n is the reciprocal of a^n. $a^{-n} = \dfrac{1}{a^n}, a \neq 0$,   so $4^{-1} = \dfrac{1}{4}$

a^n is the reciprocal of a^{-n}. $\dfrac{1}{a^{-n}} = a^n, a \neq 0$,   so $\dfrac{1}{9^{-1}} = 9^1 = 9$

Examples: $(-10)^0 = 1$ $\left(\dfrac{1}{4}\right)^{-2} = \dfrac{1}{\left(\dfrac{1}{4}\right)^2} = \dfrac{1}{\left(\dfrac{1}{16}\right)} = 16$ $\dfrac{1}{8^{-2}} = 8^2 = 64$

When **multiplying exponential terms** that have the same base, keep the base and add the exponents.

Examples: $a^2 \cdot a^3 = a^{2+3} = a^5$ $x^4 \cdot x^5 = x^{4+5} = x^9$

When **dividing exponential terms** with the same base, keep the base and subtract the exponents.

Example: $\dfrac{a^6}{a^2} = \dfrac{a \cdot a \cdot a \cdot a \cdot \not{a} \cdot \not{a}}{\not{a} \cdot \not{a}} = a \cdot a \cdot a \cdot a = a^4 = a^{6-2}$

Example: $\dfrac{b^{10}}{b^3} = b^{10-3} = b^7$

Sometimes the entire quotient is raised to a power. In that case, apply the exponent to both the numerator and denominator, simplify each of them, and then divide, if possible.

Example: $\left(\dfrac{2x^2}{5y}\right)^3 = \dfrac{\left(2x^2\right)^3}{\left(5y\right)^3} = \dfrac{2^3 \cdot \left(x^2\right)^3}{5^3 \cdot y^3} = \dfrac{8x^6}{125y^3}$

Example: $\left(\dfrac{3x^2}{9y^2}\right)^2 = \dfrac{\left(3x^2\right)^2}{\left(9y^2\right)^2} = \dfrac{3^2 \cdot \left(x^2\right)^2}{9^2 \cdot \left(y^2\right)^2} = \dfrac{\overset{}{\not{9}}x^4}{\underset{9}{\not{81}}\, y^4} = \dfrac{x^4}{9y^4}$

When **raising an exponential term to a power**, keep the base and multiply the exponents.

Examples: $\left(a^2\right)^3 = a^{2\times3} = a^6$ $\left(x^4\right)^4 = x^{4\times4} = x^{16}$

Expressions

An **expression** is a number, a variable, or any combination of these, along with operation signs $(+, -, \times, \div)$ and grouping symbols. An expression never includes an equal sign.

Five examples of expressions are 5, x, $(x + 5)$, $(3x + 5)$, and $(3x^2 + 5)$.

To **evaluate an expression** means to calculate its value using specific variable values.

Example: Evaluate $2x + 3y + 5$ when $x = 2$ and $y = 3$.

$2(2) + 3(3) + 5 = ?$

$4 + 9 + 5 = ?$

$13 + 5 = 18$

The expression has a value of 18.

1. To evaluate, put the values of x and y into the expression.
2. Use the rules for integers to calculate the value of the expression.

Help Pages

Solved Examples

Expressions (continued)

Some expressions can be made more simple. There are a few processes for **simplifying an expression**. Deciding which process or processes to use depends on the expression itself. With practice, recognizing which of the following processes to use will become easier.

The **distributive property** is used when one term is multiplied by (or divided into) an expression that includes either addition or subtraction. $a(b+c) = ab + ac$ or $\dfrac{b+c}{a} = \dfrac{b}{a} + \dfrac{c}{a}$

Example: Simplify. 3(2x + 5)

$$3(2x + 5) =$$
$$3(2x) + 3(5) =$$
$$6x + 15$$

Example: Simplify. 2(7x – 3y + 4)

$$2(7x - 3y + 4) =$$
$$2(7x) + 2(-3y) + 2(+4) =$$
$$14x - 6y + 8$$

1. Since the 3 is multiplied by the expression, 2x + 5, the 3 must be multiplied by both terms in the expression.

2. Multiply 3 by 2x, and then multiply 3 by + 5.

3. The result includes both of these: 6x + 15. Notice that simplifying an expression does not result in a single number answer, only a more simple expression.

Expressions which contain like terms can also be simplified. **Like terms** are those that contain the same variable to the same power. $2x$ and $-4x$ are like terms; $3n^2$ and $8n^2$ are like terms; $5y$ and y are like terms; 3 and 7 are like terms.

An expression sometimes begins with like terms. This process for simplifying expressions is called **combining like terms**. When combining like terms, first identify the like terms. Then, simply add the like terms to each other and write the results together to form a new expression.

Example: Simplify. 2x + 5y – 9 + 5x – 3y – 2

The like terms are 2x and +5x, +5y and –3y, and –9 and –2.

$2x + +5x = +7x$, $+5y + -3y = +2y$, and $-9 + -2 = -11$.

The result is **7x + 2y – 11**.

The next examples are a bit more complex. It is necessary to use the distributive property first, and then to combine like terms.

Example: Simplify. $2(3x + 2y + 2) + 3(2x + 3y + 2)$

$$6x + 4y + 4$$
$$+6x + 9y + 6$$
$$\overline{12x + 13y + 10}$$

1. First, apply the distributive property to each expression. Write the results on top of each other, lining up the like terms with each other. Pay attention to the signs of the terms.

2. Then, add each group of like terms. Remember to follow the rules for integers.

Example: Simplify. $4(3x - 5y - 4) - 2(3x - 3y + 2)$

$$+12x - 20y - 16$$
$$-6x + 6y - 4$$
$$\overline{6x - 14y - 20}$$

Help Pages

Solved Examples

Expressions (continued)

Other expressions that can be simplified are written as fractions. **Simplifying** these expressions (**algebraic fractions**) is similar to simplifying numerical fractions. It involves cancelling out factors that are common to both the numerator and the denominator.

Simplify. $\dfrac{12x^2yz^4}{16xy^3z^2}$

$$\frac{\overset{3}{\cancel{12}}\ \overset{x}{\cancel{x^2}}\ \cancel{y}\ \overset{z^2}{\cancel{z^4}}}{\underset{4}{\cancel{16}}\ \cancel{x}\ \underset{y^2}{\cancel{y^3}}\ \cancel{z^2}}$$

$$\frac{\cancel{2}\cdot\cancel{2}\cdot 3\cdot\cancel{x}\cdot x\cdot\cancel{y}\cdot\cancel{z}\cdot\cancel{z}\cdot z\cdot z}{\cancel{2}\cdot\cancel{2}\cdot 2\cdot 2\cdot\cancel{x}\cdot\cancel{y}\cdot y\cdot y\cdot\cancel{z}\cdot\cancel{z}}$$

$$\frac{3xz^2}{4y^2}$$

1. Begin by looking at the numerals in both the numerator and denominator (12 and 16). What is the largest number that goes into both evenly? Cancel this factor (4) out of both.

2. Look at the x portion of both numerator and denominator. What is the largest number of x's that can go into both of them? Cancel this factor (x) out of both.

3. Do the same process with y and then z. Cancel out the largest number of each (y and z^2). Write the numbers that remain in the numerator or denominator for the answer.

Often a relationship is described using verbal phrases. In order to work with the relationship, first **translate it into an algebraic expression or equation**. In most cases, word clues will be helpful. Some examples of verbal phrases and their corresponding algebraic expressions or equations are written below.

<u>Verbal Phrase</u>	<u>Algebraic Expression</u>
Ten more than a number	$x + 10$
The sum of a number and five	$x + 5$
A number increased by seven	$x + 7$
Six less than a number	$x - 6$
A number decreased by nine	$x - 9$
The difference between a number and four	$x - 4$
The difference between four and a number	$4 - x$
Five times a number	$5x$
Eight times a number, increased by one	$8x + 1$
The product of a number and six is twelve.	$6x = 12$
The quotient of a number and 10	$\dfrac{x}{10}$
The quotient of a number and two, decreased by five	$\dfrac{x}{2} - 5$

In most problems, the word "is" tells you to put in an equal sign. When working with fractions and percents, the word "of" generally means multiply. Look at the example below.

One half <u>of</u> a number <u>is</u> fifteen.

Think of it as "one half <u>times</u> a number <u>equals</u> fifteen."

When written as an algebraic equation, it is $\frac{1}{2}x = 15$.

Help Pages

Solved Examples

Expressions (continued)

At times, finding the **greatest common factor (GCF) of an algebraic expression** is needed.

Example: Find the GCF of $12x^2yz^3$ and $18xy^3z^2$.

1. First, find the GCF of the numbers (12 and 18). The largest number that is a factor of both is **6**.
2. Now look at the x's. Of the x-terms, which contains fewer x's? Comparing x^2 and x, x has fewer.
3. Now look at the y's and then the z's. Again, of the y-terms, **y** contains fewer. Of the z-terms, **z^2** has fewer.
4. The GCF contains all of these. **$6xyz^2$**

$\underline{12x^2yz^3 \text{ and } 18xy^3z^2}$

The GCF of 12 and 18 is **6**.

Of x^2 and x, the smaller is x.

Of y and y^3, the smaller is y.

Of z^3 and z^2, the smaller is z^2.

The GCF is $6xyz^2$.

At other times, finding the **least common multiple (LCM) of an algebraic expression** is called for.

Example: Find the LCM of $10a^3b^2c^2$ and $15ab^4c$.

1. First, find the LCM of the numbers (10 and 15). The lowest number that both go into evenly is **30**.
2. Now look at the a-terms. Which more a's? Comparing a^3 and a, a^3 has more.
3. Now look at the b's and then the c's. Again, of the b-terms, b^4 contains more. Of the c-terms, c^2 contains more.
4. The LCM contains all of these. **$30a^3b^4c^2$**.

$\underline{10a^3b^2c^2 \text{ and } 15ab^4c}$

The LCM of 10 and 15 is **30**. Of a^3 and a, the larger is a^3.

Of b^2 and b^4, the larger is b^4.

Of c^2 and c, the larger is c^2.

The LCM is $30a^3b^4c^2$.

When **adding (subtracting) rational expressions**, the process is similar to that used to add (subtract) ordinary fractions. Just as with fractions, rational expressions must have a common denominator before they can be added (subtracted).

Example: Add. $\dfrac{5}{3x} + \dfrac{7}{3x}$

$$\frac{5}{3x} + \frac{7}{3x} = \frac{\cancel{12}}{\cancel{3}x} = \frac{4}{x}$$

1. Since the expressions already have a common denominator, they can be added.
2. Add the numerators; keep the denominator.
3. Simplify.

Example: Subtract. $\dfrac{x}{2} - \dfrac{(x-1)}{(x-2)}$

$2(x-2)$ is the common denominator.

$$\cancel{2}(x-2)\frac{x}{\cancel{2}} - 2\cancel{(x-2)}\frac{(x-1)}{\cancel{(x-2)}} =$$

$$(x-2)x - 2(x-1) =$$

$$x^2 - 2x - 2x + 2 =$$

$$x^2 - 4x + 2 =$$

$$(x-2)(x-2)$$

(simplified answer)

1. The expressions need a common denominator, before they can be added. Multiply the denominators to get a common denominator.
2. Multiply each fraction by the common denominator. Cancel where possible.
3. Simplify and combine like terms.
4. Simplify by factoring.

Help Pages

Solved Examples

Expressions (continued)

When **multiplying (dividing) rational expressions**, the process is similar to that used to multiply (divide) ordinary fractions. A common denominator is not necessary to multiply (divide) rational expressions.

Example: Multiply. $\dfrac{2x^2}{3x} \cdot \dfrac{6x^2}{12x^3}$

$$\dfrac{\cancel{12}\,\cancel{x^4}}{\cancel{36}\,\cancel{x^4}} =$$

$$\dfrac{1}{3}$$

> 1. Just as with ordinary fractions, multiply the numerators; multiply the denominators.
> 2. Cancel where possible.
> 3. Simplify.

Example: Divide. $\dfrac{7x^2 - 7x}{x^2 + 2x - 3} \div \dfrac{x+1}{x^2 - 7x - 8}$

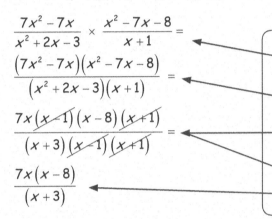

$$\dfrac{7x^2 - 7x}{x^2 + 2x - 3} \times \dfrac{x^2 - 7x - 8}{x+1} =$$

$$\dfrac{(7x^2 - 7x)(x^2 - 7x - 8)}{(x^2 + 2x - 3)(x+1)} =$$

$$\dfrac{7x\,\cancel{(x-1)}\,(x-8)\,\cancel{(x+1)}}{(x+3)\,\cancel{(x-1)}\,\cancel{(x+1)}} =$$

$$\dfrac{7x(x-8)}{(x+3)}$$

> 1. Just as with ordinary fractions, to divide, take the reciprocal of the 2nd fraction and multiply.
> 2. Multiply the numerators; multiply the denominators.
> 3. Simplify the expressions where possible by factoring.
> 4. Cancel where possible.
> 5. Simplify.

Functions

A **function** is a rule that pairs each number in a given set (the domain) with just one number in another set (the range). A function performs one or more operations on an input-number which results in an output-number. The set of all input-numbers is called the **domain** of the function. The set of all output-numbers is called the **range** of the function. Often, a function table is used to help organize the information.

Example: For the function, $y = 3x$, find the missing numbers in the function table.

The function is $y = 3x$. This function multiplies every x-value by 3.

x	y
2	?
-1	?
?	15

When $x = 2$, the result is $y = 3(2)$ or $y = 6$.

When $x = -1$, the result is $y = 3(-1)$ or $y = -3$.

When $y = 15$, the result is $15 = 3x$, so $\dfrac{15}{3} = x$ or $5 = x$.

x	y
2	?
-1	?
?	15

The set of all inputs is the domain. For this function table, the domain is {2, –1, 5}

The set of all outputs is the range. For this function table, the range is {6, –3, 15}.

Help Pages

Solved Examples

Geometry

Finding the **area of a parallelogram** is similar to finding the area of any other quadrilateral. The area of the figure is equal to the length of its base multiplied by the height of the figure.

$$\text{Area of parallelogram} = \text{base} \times \text{height} \quad \text{or} \quad A = b \times h$$

Example: Find the area of the parallelogram below.

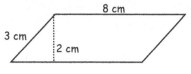

1. Find the length of the base. (8 cm)
2. Find the height. (It is 2 cm. The height is always straight up and down—never slanted.)
3. Multiply to find the area. (16 cm²)

$A = 8 \text{ cm} \times 2 \text{ cm} = \textbf{16 cm}^2$

Finding the **area of a trapezoid** is a little different than other quadrilaterals. Trapezoids have 2 bases of unequal length. To find the area, first find the average of the lengths of the 2 bases. Then, multiply that average by the height.

$$\text{Area of trapezoid} = \frac{\text{base}_1 + \text{base}_2}{2} \times \text{height} \quad \text{or} \quad A = \left(\frac{b_1 + b_2}{2}\right)h$$

Example: Find the area of the trapezoid below.

1. Add the lengths of the two bases. (22 cm)

2. Divide the sum by 2. (11 cm)

3. Multiply that result by the height to find the area. (110 cm²)

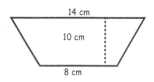

$\dfrac{14 \text{ cm} + 8 \text{ cm}}{2} = \dfrac{22 \text{ cm}}{2} = 11 \text{ cm}$

$11 \text{ cm} \times 10 \text{ cm} = \textbf{110 cm}^2 = \text{Area}$

To find the **area of a triangle**, first recognize that any triangle is exactly half of a parallelogram.

The whole figure is a parallelogram.

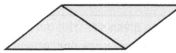

Half of the whole figure is a triangle.

The triangle's area is equal to half of the product of the base and the height.

$$\text{Area of triangle} = \frac{1}{2}(\text{base} \times \text{height}) \quad \text{or} \quad A = \frac{1}{2}bh$$

Examples: Find the area of the triangles below.

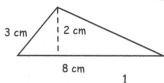

1. Find the length of the base. (8 cm)
2. Find the height. (It is 2 cm. The height is always straight up and down—never slanted.)
3. Multiply them together and divide by 2 to find the area. (8 cm²)

$A = 8 \text{ cm} \times 2 \text{ cm} \times \dfrac{1}{2} = \textbf{8 cm}^2$

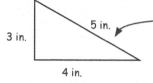

The base of this triangle is 4 inches long. Its height is 3 inches. (Remember the height is always straight up and down!)

$A = 4 \text{ in.} \times 3 \text{ in.} \times \dfrac{1}{2} = \textbf{6 in.}^2$

Help Pages

Solved Examples

Geometry (continued)

Remember there are three types of triangles: acute, obtuse, and right. **A right triangle** has one 90° angle. (The other 2 angles will be less than 90°; the sum of the angles in any triangle is 180°.) Every triangle has 3 sides; in a right triangle, the sides have names. There are two legs and a hypotenuse. The **legs** are the sides that come together to form the right angle; they are said to be adjacent to the right angle. The **hypotenuse** is the side that is opposite the right angle.

In this right triangle, sides *a* and *b* are the legs. 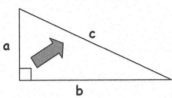 Side *c* is across from (opposite) the right angle. Side *c* is the hypotenuse.

Right triangles have many special relationships. Here, the focus will be on one relationship in particular—the relationship defined by the Pythagorean Theorem.

The **Pythagorean Theorem** states, "In any right triangle, the sum of the squares of the legs is equal to the square of the hypotenuse." To put it another way, $a^2 + b^2 = c^2$.

Example: Find the measure of the third side in this triangle.

$a^2 + b^2 = c^2$

(Note that the missing side is a leg.)

$a^2 + 4^2 = 5^2$

$a^2 + 16 = 25$

$a^2 = 9$

$a = \sqrt{9} = 3$ (Remember: To undo a square, find the square root.)

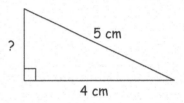

Example: Find the measure of the third side in this triangle.

$a^2 + b^2 = c^2$

(Note that the missing side is the hypotenuse.)

$5^2 + 6^2 = c^2$

$25 + 36 = c^2$

$61 = c^2$

$\sqrt{61} = c$

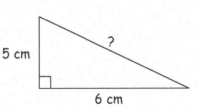

Help Pages

Solved Examples

Geometry (continued)

The **circumference of a circle** is the distance around the outside of the circle. Before you can find the circumference of a circle either its radius or its diameter must be known. The value of the constant, pi (π) $\pi = 3.14$ (rounded to the nearest hundredth) must be known.

Once you have this information, the circumference can be found by multiplying the diameter by pi.

Circumference = $\pi \times$ diameter or $C = \pi d$

Examples: Find the circumference of the circles below.

1. Find the length of the diameter. (12 m)
2. Multiply the diameter by π. (12 m × 3.14)
3. The product is the circumference. (37.68 m)

$C = 12$ m × 3.14 = **37.68 m**

Sometimes the radius of a circle is given instead of the diameter. The radius of any circle is exactly half of the diameter. If a circle has a radius of 3 feet, its diameter is 6 feet.

1. Since the radius is 4 mm, the diameter must be 8 mm.
2. Multiply the diameter by π. (8 mm × 3.14)
3. The product is the circumference. (25.12 mm)

$C = 8$ mm × 3.14 = **25.12 mm**

When finding the **area of a circle**, the length of the radius is squared (multiplied by itself), and then that answer is multiplied by the constant, pi (π). $\pi = 3.14$ (rounded to the nearest hundredth).

Area = $\pi \times$ radius × radius or $A = \pi r^2$

Examples: Find the area of the circles below.

1. Find the length of the radius. (9 mm)
2. Multiply the radius by itself. (9 mm x 9 mm)
3. Multiply the product by pi. (81 mm² x 3.14)
4. The result is the area. (254.34 mm²)

$A = 9$ mm x 9 mm x 3.14 = **254.34 mm²**

Sometimes the diameter of a circle is given instead of the radius. Remember, the diameter of any circle is exactly twice the radius. If a circle has a diameter of 6 feet, its radius is 3 feet.

1. Since the diameter is 14 m, the radius must be 7 m.
2. Square the radius. (7 m x 7 m)
3. Multiply that result by π. (49 m² × 3.14).
4. The product is the area. (153.86 m²)

$A = (7$ m$)^2$ x 3.14 = **153.86 m²**

Help Pages

Solved Examples

Geometry (continued)

To find the **surface area** of a solid figure, it is necessary to first count the total number of faces. Then, find the area of each of the faces; finally, add the areas of each face. That sum is the surface area of the figure.

Here, the focus will be on finding the **surface area of a rectangular prism**. A rectangular prism has 6 faces. Actually, the opposite faces are identical, so this figure has 3 pairs of faces. Also, a prism has only 3 dimensions: length, width, and height.

This prism has identical left and right sides (A & B), identical top and bottom (C & D), and identical front and back (unlabeled).

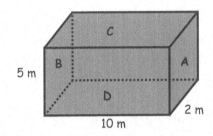

5 m
10 m
2 m

1. Find the area of the front: $l \times w$. (10 m x 5 m = 50 m²)
   Since the back is identical, its area is the same.

2. Find the area of the top (C): $l \times h$. (10 m x 2 m = 20 m²)
   Since the bottom (D) is identical, its area is the same.

3. Find the area of side A: $w \times h$. (2 m x 5 m = 10 m²)
   Since side B is identical, its area is the same.

4. Add up the areas of all 6 faces.
   (10 m² + 10 m² + 20 m² + 20 m² + 50 m² + 50 m² = 160 m²)

The formula is Surface Area = 2(length x width) + 2(length x height) + 2(width x height)

or $SA = 2lw + 2lh + 2wh$.

To find the volume of a solid figure, it is necessary to determine the area one face and multiply that by the height of the figure. Volume of a solid is measured in cubic units (cm³, in.³, ft³, etc.).

Here the focus will be on finding the **volume of a cylinder**. As shown below, a cylinder has two identical circular faces.

Example: Find the volume of the cylinder below.

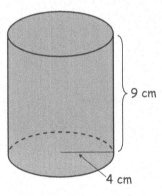

9 cm
4 cm

1. To find the area of one of the circular faces, multiply the constant, π (3.14), by the square of the radius (4 cm). Area = 3.14 × (4 cm)² = 50.24 cm²

2. The height of this cylinder is 9 cm. Multiply the height by the area calculated in Step 1.

3. Volume = 50.24 cm² × 9 cm = 452.16 cm³

Help Pages

Solved Examples

Graphing

A **coordinate plane** is formed by the intersection of a horizontal number line, called the **x-axis**, and a vertical number line, called the **y-axis**. The axes meet at the point (0, 0), called the **origin**, and divide the coordinate plane into four **quadrants**.

Points are represented by **ordered pairs** of numbers, (x, y). The first number in an ordered pair is the x-coordinate; the second number is the y-coordinate. In the point (-4, 1), -4 is the x-coordinate, and 1 is the y-coordinate.

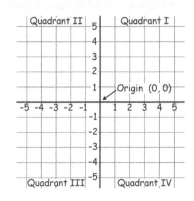

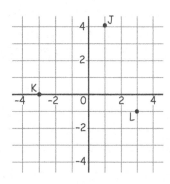

When graphing on a coordinate plane, always move on the x-axis first (right or left), and then move on the y-axis (up or down).

- The coordinates of point J are (1, 4).
- The coordinates of point K are (-3, 0).
- The coordinates of point L are (3, -1).

On a coordinate plane, any 2 points can be connected to form a line. The line, however, is made up of many points—in fact, every place on the line is another point. One of the properties of a line is its slope (or steepness). The **slope** of a non-vertical line is the ratio of its vertical change (rise) to its horizontal change (run) between any two points on the line. The slope of a line is represented by the letter m. Another property of a line is the **y-intercept**. This is the point where the line intersects the y-axis. A line has only one y-intercept, which is represented by the letter b.

$$\text{Slope of a line} = \frac{\text{change in } y}{\text{change in } x} = \frac{\text{rise}}{\text{run}}$$

The rise-over-run method can be used to find the slope if looking at a graph.

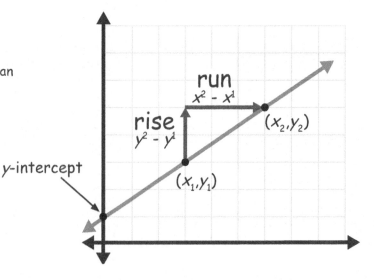

Help Pages

Solved Examples

Graphing (continued)

Another way to find the slope of a line is to use a formula. The formula for slope is $m = \dfrac{y_2 - y_1}{x_2 - x_1}$, where the two points are (x_1, y_1) and (x_2, y_2).

Example: What is the slope of $\overline{AD}$?

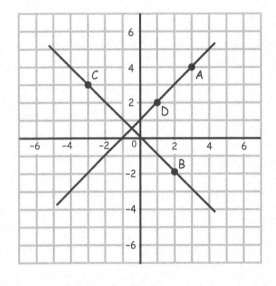

Point A with coordinates (3, 4) and Point D with coordinates (1, 2) are both on this line.

For Point A, x_2 is 3 and y_2 is 4.
For Point B, x_1 is 1 and y_1 is 2.

slope = $m = \dfrac{y_2 - y_1}{x_2 - x_1} = \dfrac{4-2}{3-1} = \dfrac{2}{2} = 1$

The slope of $\overline{AD}$ is 1.

Use the formula to find the slope of $\overline{CB}$.

Point C is (-3, 3), and Point B is (2, -2).

slope = $m = \dfrac{y_2 - y_1}{x_2 - x_1} = \dfrac{-2-3}{2-(-3)} = \dfrac{-5}{5} = -1$

The slope of $\overline{CB}$ is -1.

Every line has an equation which describes it, called a linear equation. One particular form of linear equation is called the **slope-intercept form**. To write the slope-intercept equation of a line, the slope and the y-intercept must be known.

A linear equation in slope-intercept form is always in the form $y = mx + b$, where m is the slope, b is the y-intercept, and (x, y) is any point on the line.

Example: A line has the equation $y = 2x + 5$. What is the slope? What is the y-intercept?

$$y = 2x + 5$$
$$\uparrow \quad \uparrow$$
$$y = mx + b$$

The slope, m, is 2. The y-intercept, b, is 5.

Example: A line has a slope of 6 and a y-intercept of -3. Write the equation for the line.

The slope is 6, so $m = 6$. The y-intercept is -3, so $b = -3$.
Put those values into the slope-intercept form. $y = 6x - 3$

Example: Write the equation of a line that passes through points (3, 2) and (6, 4).

Only 2 things are needed to write the equation of a line: slope and y-intercept.

First, find the slope. $m = \dfrac{y_2 - y_1}{x_2 - x_1} = \dfrac{4-2}{6-3} = \dfrac{2}{3}$

Then, find the y-intercept. Choose either point. Use (6, 4). The x-value of this point is 6, and the y-value is 4. Put these values along with the slope into the equation and solve for b.

$y = mx + b$ $4 = \dfrac{2}{3}(6) + b$ $4 = \dfrac{12}{3} + b$ $4 = 4 + b$ $0 = b$

The slope = $\dfrac{2}{3}$, and the y-intercept = 0. The equation of the line is $y = \dfrac{2}{3}x + 0$.

Help Pages

Solved Examples

Inequalities

An inequality is a statement that one quantity is different from another (usually larger or smaller). The symbols showing inequality are <, >, ≤, and ≥ (less than, greater than, less than or equal to, and greater than or equal to.) An inequality is formed by placing one of the inequality symbols between two expressions. The solution of an inequality is the set of numbers that can be substituted for the variable to make the statement true.

A simple inequality is $x \leq 4$. The solution set, {..., 2, 3, 4}, includes all numbers that are either less than four or equal to four.

Some inequalities are solved using only addition or subtraction. The approach to solving them is similar to that used when solving equations. The goal is to get the variable alone on one side of the inequality and the numbers on the other side.

Examples: Solve. $x - 4 < 8$

$$
\begin{array}{rl}
x - 4 & < 8 \\
+ 4 & + 4 \\
\hline
x & < 12
\end{array}
$$

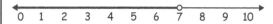

1. To get the variable alone, add the opposite of the number that is with it to both sides.
2. Simplify both sides of the inequality.
3. Graph the solution on a number line. For < and >, use an open circle; for ≤ and ≥, use a closed circle.

Solve. $y + 3 \geq 10$

$$
\begin{array}{rl}
y + 3 & \geq 10 \\
- 3 & - 3 \\
\hline
y & \geq 7
\end{array}
$$

Some inequalities are solved using only multiplication or division. The approach to solving them is also similar to that used when solving equations. Here, too, the goal is to get the variable alone on one side of the inequality and the numbers on the other side.

The one difference to remember is this: If, when solving a problem multiplication or division by a negative number is used, the inequality symbol must be flipped.

Examples: Solve. $8n < 56$

1. Check to see if the variable is being multiplied or divided by a number.
2. Use the same number, but do the opposite operation on both sides.

$$\frac{8n}{8} < \frac{56}{8}$$
$$n < 7$$

3. Simplify both sides of the inequality.
4. Graph the solution on a number line. For < and >, use an open circle; for ≤ and ≥, use a closed circle.

Solve. $\dfrac{x}{-6} > 4$

$$\frac{x}{-6} > 4$$

$$(-6)\frac{x}{-6} < 4(-6)$$

$$x < -24$$

Notice that during the 2nd step, when multiplying by -6, the sign "flipped" from greater than to less than.

(number line: 0 1 2 3 4 5 6 7 8 9 10 with open circle at 7)

(number line: -30 -29 -28 -27 -26 -25 -24 -23 -22 -21 -23 with open circle at -24)

REMEMBER: When multiplying or dividing an inequality by a negative number, the inequality symbol must be flipped!

Help Pages

Solved Examples

Inequalities (continued)

Some inequalities must be solved using both addition/subtraction and multiplication/division. In these problems, the addition/subtraction is always done first.

Example: $2x - 6 \leq 6$

$$
\begin{array}{r}
2x - 6 \leq 6 \\
+6 \quad +6 \\
\hline
2x \quad \leq 12
\end{array}
$$

$$\frac{2x}{2} \quad \leq \frac{12}{2}$$

$$x \quad \leq 6$$

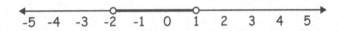

A **compound inequality** is a statement comparing one quantity (in the middle) with two other quantities (on either side).

$-2 < y < 1$ This can be read "y is greater than -2, but less than 1."

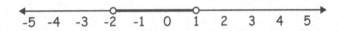

Integers

The rules for performing operations $(+, -, \times, \div)$ on integers are very important and must be memorized.

The Addition Rules for Integers:

1. When the signs are the same, add the numbers and keep the sign.

$$
\begin{array}{r}
+33 \\
+ +19 \\
\hline
+52
\end{array}
\qquad
\begin{array}{r}
-33 \\
+ -19 \\
\hline
-52
\end{array}
$$

2. When the signs are different, subtract the numbers and use the sign of the larger number.

$$
\begin{array}{r}
+33 \\
+ -19 \\
\hline
+14
\end{array}
\qquad
\begin{array}{r}
-55 \\
+ +27 \\
\hline
-28
\end{array}
$$

The Subtraction Rule for Integers:

Change the sign of the second number and add (follow the Addition Rule for Integers above).

$$
\begin{array}{r}
+56 \\
- -26 \\
\hline
\end{array}
\xrightarrow{\text{apply rule}}
\begin{array}{r}
+56 \\
+ +26 \\
\hline
+82
\end{array}
\qquad
\begin{array}{r}
+48 \\
- +23 \\
\hline
\end{array}
\xrightarrow{\text{apply rule}}
\begin{array}{r}
+48 \\
+ -23 \\
\hline
+25
\end{array}
$$

Notice that every subtraction problem becomes an addition problem, using this rule!

The Multiplication and Division Rule for Integers:

1. When the signs are the same, the answer is positive (+).

$$+7 \times +3 = +21 \qquad -7 \times -3 = +21$$
$$+18 \div +6 = +3 \qquad -18 \div -6 = +3$$

2. When the signs are different, the answer is negative (-).

$$+7 \times -3 = -21 \qquad -7 \times +3 = -21$$
$$-18 \div +6 = -3 \qquad +18 \div -6 = -3$$

The chart to the right contains a helpful summary of this rule.

+		+		+
−	×	−		+
+		−	=	−
−		+		−
+		+		+
−	÷	−		+
+		−		−
−		+		−

Help Pages

Solved Examples

Matrix, Matrices

A **matrix** is a rectangular arrangement of numbers in rows and columns. Each number in a matrix is an element or entry. The plural of matrix is **matrices**.

$$\begin{pmatrix} 0 & 4 & -1 \\ -3 & 2 & 5 \end{pmatrix}$$

The matrix to the right has 2 rows and 3 columns. It has 6 elements.

In order to be added or subtracted, matrices must have the same number of rows and columns. If they don't have the same dimensions, they cannot be added or subtracted.

When **adding matrices**, simply add corresponding elements.

Example: $\begin{pmatrix} 0 & 4 & -1 \\ -3 & 2 & 5 \end{pmatrix} + \begin{pmatrix} 2 & 1 & 3 \\ -2 & -6 & 4 \end{pmatrix} = \begin{pmatrix} (0+2) & (4+1) & (-1+3) \\ (-3+(-2)) & (2+(-6)) & (5+4) \end{pmatrix} = \begin{pmatrix} 2 & 5 & 2 \\ -5 & -4 & 9 \end{pmatrix}$

When subtracting matrices, remember the subtraction rule for integers. A simple way to subtract matrices is to change the signs of every element of the second matrix. Then change the operation to addition and follow the rule for addition of integers (as shown in the previous example).

Example: First <u>change all signs</u>, then add.

$$\begin{pmatrix} -10 & 2 \\ 3 & -7 \end{pmatrix} - \begin{pmatrix} 5 & -3 \\ 6 & -1 \end{pmatrix} = \begin{pmatrix} -10 & 2 \\ 3 & -7 \end{pmatrix} + \begin{pmatrix} -5 & +3 \\ -6 & +1 \end{pmatrix} = \begin{pmatrix} (-10+(-5)) & (2+3) \\ (3+(-6)) & (-7+1) \end{pmatrix} = \begin{pmatrix} -15 & +5 \\ -3 & -6 \end{pmatrix}$$

Percent

Percent of change shows how much a quantity has increased or decreased from its original amount. When the new amount is greater than the original amount, the percent of change is called the **percent of increase**. When the new amount is less than the original amount, the percent of change is called the **percent of decrease**. Both of these are found in the same way. The difference between the new amount and the original amount is divided by the original amount. The result is multiplied by 100 to get the percent of change.

$$\text{Formula: \% of change} = \frac{\text{amount of increase or decrease}}{\text{original amount}} \times 100$$

Example: A sapling measured 23 inches tall when it was planted. Two years later the sapling was 36 inches tall. What was the percent of increase? Round the answer to a whole number.

$$\left(\frac{36-23}{23} \right) \times 100 =$$

$$\left(\frac{13}{23} \right) \times 100 = 0.565$$

$$0.565 \times 100 = 57\% \quad \text{The sapling's height increased by 57\% over the 2 years.}$$

Polynomials

A **polynomial** is the sum of one or more monomials. Remember that a monomial is a number, a variable, or the product of numbers and variables with or without exponents. Here are some examples of monomials ($3x$, 7, $2xy$, $2y^2$, x^3). Polynomials may have any number of terms.

A **binomial** is a polynomial with exactly 2 terms. Examples: $3x - 7$, $2x + 5y$, $2y^2 + x^3$

A **trinomial** is a polynomial with exactly 3 terms. Examples: $3x^2 - 7 + 2x$, $5y + 2y^2 - x^3$

Help Pages

Solved Examples

Polynomials (continued)

When **adding polynomials**, simply combine like terms. It is helpful to line up the like terms before adding.

Example: Add the polynomials.

$$\begin{array}{r} 2x^3 - 6x^2 + x \\ + 3x^3 - 2x^2 \quad\; - 3 \\ \hline 5x^3 - 8x^2 + x - 3 \end{array}$$

To subtract polynomials, use the subtraction rule for integers (change the sign of every term in the second polynomial and add).

Example: Subtract the polynomials.

$$\begin{array}{r} 6n^2 - 4n + 5 \\ - 2n^2 + 2n \;\; - 3 \\ \hline \end{array} \Longrightarrow \begin{array}{r} 6n^2 - 4n + 5 \\ + \; -2n^2 - 2n \;\; + 3 \\ \hline 4n^2 - 6n \;\; + 8 \end{array}$$

When **multiplying polynomials**, multiply each term in the first polynomial by each term in the second polynomial, and then combine like terms. (The process is similar to long multiplication.)

Example: Multiply. $(2b - 2)(b^2 + 4b - 5)$

$$\begin{array}{r} b^2 + 4b - 5 \\ \times \quad\;\; 2b - 2 \\ \hline -2b^2 - 8b + 10 \\ + \; 2b^3 + 8b^2 - 10b \\ \hline 2b^3 + 6b^2 - 18b + 10 \end{array}$$

When **multiplying two binomials**, the **FOIL method** can be used. In the FOIL method, the First terms in each binomial are multiplied, the Outer terms in each binomial are multiplied, the Inner terms in each binomial are multiplied, and then the Last terms in each binomial are multiplied; finally all like terms are combined to get the product.

Example: Multiply using the FOIL method. $(3a + 4)(a - 2)$

The first terms are $3a$ and a ; their product is **$3a^2$**.

The outer terms are $3a$ and -2; their product is **$-6a$**.

The inner terms are 4 and a ; their product is **$4a$**.

The last terms are 4 and -2; their product is **-8**.

The sum of these is $3a^2 + (-6a) + 4a + (-8)$. The product of the binomials is **$3a^2 - 2a - 8$**.

Example: Multiply using the FOIL method. $(2x - 1)(5x + 3)$

The first terms are $2x$ and $5x$; their product is **$10x^2$**.

The outer terms are $2x$ and 3; their product is **$6x$**.

The inner terms are -1 and $5x$; their product is **$-5x$**.

The last terms are -1 and 3; their product is **-3**.

The sum of these is $10x^2 + 6x + (-5x) + (-3)$.

The product of the binomials is a trinomial: **$10x^2 + x - 3$**.

Help Pages

Solved Examples

Polynomials (continued)

The process of **factoring polynomials** is the reverse of multiplying them. Factoring means trying to find the simplest factors that can be multiplied together to get a polynomial.

Sometimes factoring is as easy as finding the largest common factor in each term and dividing all of the terms by that factor. This process is "undoing" the distributive property. When factoring any polynomial, first check to see if there is a common factor that can easily be divided out.

Example: Factor. $9x^2 + 6x = \dfrac{\cancel{9}^{3x} \cancel{x^2}}{\cancel{3}\,\cancel{x}} + \dfrac{\cancel{6}^{2} \cancel{x}}{\cancel{3}\,\cancel{x}} = 3x(3x + 2)$

The largest factor that goes into both terms is $3x$. Divide each term by $3x$. This results in the two prime factors: $3x$ and $3x + 2$

Once checked for any common factors, some trinomials can be factored further. The process of factoring a trinomial can be thought of as "undoing" the FOIL method. Look for 2 binomials that can be multiplied together to get the trinomial.

To understand this, look at this trinomial. $x^2 + 5x + 6$

This trinomial is the product of 2 binomials: $(x + 3)$ and $(x + 2)$.
Where does each term in the trinomial come from?

The 1st term in the trinomial is the product of the 1st terms in the binomials: $x \cdot x = x^2$.

The last term in the trinomial is the product of the 2nd terms in the binomials: $3(2) = 6$.

The middle term in the trinomial is the sum of the product of the inner terms $(3 \cdot x = 3x)$ and the product of the outer terms $(2 \cdot x = 2x)$ in the binomials: $3x + 2x = 5x$.

One way of representing this is $(a + b)(c + d) = ac + (bc + ad) + bd$.

Try to apply it to a different trinomial. Factor. $x^2 + 11x + 18$

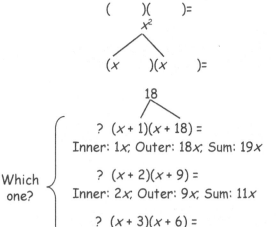

$x^2 + 11x + 18$
The answer will be in this form:
$(\quad)(\quad)=$

$(x \quad)(x \quad)=$

18

? $(x + 1)(x + 18) =$
Inner: $1x$; Outer: $18x$; Sum: $19x$

Which one?

? $(x + 2)(x + 9) =$
Inner: $2x$; Outer: $9x$; Sum: $11x$

? $(x + 3)(x + 6) =$
Inner: $3x$; Outer: $6x$; Sum: $9x$

All of these are factors of 18. Which one results in the correct middle term?

1. Check to see if there is a factor common to all three terms. If so, factor it out. (There isn't.)
2. Look at the first term (x^2). What 2 terms can be multiplied to get x^2? $x \cdot x$ are the only factors. x will be the 1st term in both binomials.
3. Look at the last term (18). What 2 factors can be multiplied to get 18? There are several pairs of possibilities: 1 and 18, 2 and 9, 3 and 6. The 2nd terms in the binomials will come from these.
4. To choose the correct pair of factors, remember that each will be multiplied by the first terms, and those products must add to the middle term.
5. The middle term is $11x$, so 2 and 9 must be the correct pair.

$$(x + 2)(x + 9) = x^2 + 11x + 18$$

Help Pages

Solved Examples

Polynomials (continued)

Example: What are the factors of $n^2 + 2n - 15$?

- The factors of n^2 are $n \cdot n$. $(n\quad)(n\quad)=$
- The factors of -15 are 1 & -15,
  -1 & 15, 3 & -5, and -3 & 5.
- Each pair, multiplied by n, and $(n - 3)(n + 5) =$
  added gives: $1n + -15n = -14n$,
  $-1n + 15n = 14n$, $3n + -5n = -2n$,
  $-3n + 5n = 2n$.

Since $2n$ is the correct middle term, the correct pair of factors is -3 and 5.

Some polynomials can be a bit more complicated to factor.
These are usually in the form of $ax^2 + bx + c$, where a is not 1. The process for factoring these polynomials is the same as those above, but there are many more possible factors to consider.

Example: Find the factors of $2x^2 - 7x + 3$.

1. The factors of $2x^2$ are $2x$ and x. $(2x\quad)(x\quad)=$

2. The factors of 3 are 1 & 3 and -1 & -3.
   Each combination of factors must be
   considered. Multiply the outer terms,
   then the inner terms and add them:

- Look at the combinations involving 1 & 3.   The possible combinations are
  $2x \cdot 1 = 2x$; $x \cdot 3 = 3x$; their sum is $5x$. $(2x + 3)(x + 1)$
  $2x \cdot 3 = 6x$; $x \cdot 1 = 1x$; their sum is $7x$.   or   Neither works.
  Neither of these is correct. $(2x + 1)(x + 3)$

- Look at the combinations involving -1 & -3.   The possible combinations are
  $2x \cdot -1 = -2x$; $x \cdot -3 = -3x$; their sum is $-5x$. $(2x - 3)(x - 1)$
  $2x \cdot -3 = -6x$; $x \cdot -1 = -1x$; their sum is $-7x$.   or
  The last pairing is the correct one! $(2x - 1)(x - 3)$ The last pair works.

The **difference of two squares** represents a special type of polynomial. This is a binomial where both terms are perfect squares, one term is positive, and one term is negative. When factoring a polynomial in this form $(a^2 - b^2)$, the results are always $(a + b)(a - b)$.

Example 1: What are the factors of $y^2 - 16$?

The first term, y^2, is a perfect square. y^2 $(y +\quad)(y -\quad)$

The last term, 16, is a perfect square. $16 = 4^2$ $(y + 4)(y - 4)$

Example 2: What are the factors of $49m^2 - 36$?

The first term, $49m^2$, is a perfect square. $(7m)^2$ $(7m +\quad)(7m -\quad)$

The last term, 36, is a perfect square. $36 = 6^2$ $(7m + 6)(7m - 6)$

Help Pages

Solved Examples

Compound Probability

The **probability of two or more independent events** occurring together can be determined by multiplying the individual probabilities together. The product is called the **compound probability**.

$$P(A \text{ and } B) = P(A) \times P(B)$$

Example: What is the probability of rolling a 6 and then a 2 on two rolls of a die [P(6 and 2)]?

    A) First, find the probability of rolling a 6 [P(6)]. Since there are 6 numbers on a die and only one of them is a 6, the probability of getting a 6 is $\frac{1}{6}$.

    B) Then find the probability of rolling a 2 [P(2)]. Since there are 6 numbers on a die and only one of them is a 2, the probability of getting a 2 is $\frac{1}{6}$.

$$P(6 \text{ and } 2) = P(6) \times P(2) = \frac{1}{6} \times \frac{1}{6} = \frac{1}{36}$$

There is a 1 to 36 chance of getting a 6 and then a 2 on two rolls of a die.

Example: In a bag of 10 marbles, 4 green and 6 blue, what is the probability of picking a green marble and then a blue one without replacement?

    A) First, the probability of picking a green marble is $\frac{4}{10}$.

    B) Without replacing the first pick, there are now only 9 marbles in the bag, so the probability of picking a blue marble is $\frac{6}{9}$.

The probability is $\frac{6}{10} \times \frac{4}{9} = \frac{24}{90} = \frac{4}{15}$.

There is a 4 to 15 chance of picking a green and then a blue marble without replacement.

Radicals

A **radical expression** is an expression that contains a radical, such as a square root, cubed root, or other root. Radical expressions can be added, subtracted, multiplied, divided, and simplified much like rational expressions.

The square root of a number is equal to the product of the square root of its factor.

Example: $\sqrt{4x} = \sqrt{4} \cdot \sqrt{x} = 2\sqrt{x}$

Example: $\sqrt{32} = \sqrt{16 \cdot 2} = \sqrt{16} \cdot \sqrt{2} = 4\sqrt{2}$

Example: $\sqrt{9x^3} = \sqrt{9 \cdot x^2 \cdot x} = \sqrt{9} \cdot \sqrt{x^2} \cdot \sqrt{x} = 3x\sqrt{x}$

When **adding (subtracting) radical expressions**, the numbers under the radical must be the same or they can't be combined. This requires simplifying the radical first. Once the numbers under the radical are the same, the coefficients are added (subtracted) and the radical kept the same.

Example: Add. $3\sqrt{2} + 5\sqrt{2} = 8\sqrt{2}$

Example: Add. $5\sqrt{3} + \sqrt{48}$

$$5\sqrt{3} + \sqrt{16 \cdot 3} =$$
$$5\sqrt{3} + \sqrt{16} \cdot \sqrt{3} =$$
$$5\sqrt{3} + 4\sqrt{3} =$$
$$9\sqrt{3}$$

1. If the numbers under the radical are different, they must be simplified first.
2. Factor the numbers under the radical, looking for perfect squares.
3. If there are perfect squares, simplify.
4. Once the numbers beneath the radical are the same, add the coefficients.

Help Pages

Solved Examples

Radicals (continued)

Example: $3\sqrt{7} - 5\sqrt{14} + 2\sqrt{28}$

$3\sqrt{7} - 5\sqrt{14} + 2\sqrt{28} =$

$3\sqrt{7} - 5\sqrt{7 \cdot 2} + 2\sqrt{4 \cdot 7} =$

$3\sqrt{7} - 5\sqrt{14} + 2\sqrt{4} \cdot \sqrt{7} =$

$3\sqrt{7} - 5\sqrt{14} + 4\sqrt{7} =$

$7\sqrt{7} - 5\sqrt{14}$

Although $5\sqrt{14}$ can be broken down into factors, none of them is a perfect square, so $5\sqrt{14}$ is as simple as it can be.

Scientific Notation

Scientific notation is a shorthand method for representing numbers that are either very large or very small—numbers that have many zeros and are tedious to write out.

For example, 5,000,000,000 and 0.000000023 have so many zeros that it is not convenient to write them this way. Scientific notation removes the "placeholder" zeros and represents them as powers of 10. Numbers in scientific notation always have the form $c \times 10^n$ where $1 \le c < 10$ and n is an integer.

Examples: $5{,}000{,}000{,}000 = 5 \times 10^9$ $0.000000023 = 2.3 \times 10^{-8}$

5,000,000,000	1. First locate the decimal point. Remember, if the decimal point isn't shown, it is after the last digit on the right.	0.000000023
5.000,000,000.	2. Move the decimal point (either left or right) until the number is at least 1 and less than 10.	0.00000002.3
5×10^9	3. Count the number of places you moved the decimal point. This is the exponent.	2.3×10^{-8}
	4. If you moved the decimal to the right, the exponent will be negative; if you moved it to the left, the exponent will be positive.	
The decimal point was moved 9 places to the left, so the exponent is +9.	5. Write the number times 10 to the power of the exponent that you found.	The decimal point was moved 8 places to the right, so the exponent is -8.

Who Knows?

Degrees in a right angle? ....(90)

A straight angle? ....(180)

Angle greater than 90°? ....(obtuse)

Less than 90°? ....(acute)

Sides in a quadrilateral? ....(4)

Sides in an octagon?........................ (8)

Sides in a hexagon? ....(6)

Sides in a pentagon? ....(5)

Sides in a heptagon? ....(7)

Sides in a nonagon? .... (9)

Sides in a decagon?......................... (10)

Inches in a yard? ....(36)

Yards in a mile? ....(1,760)

Feet in a mile? ....(5,280)

Centimeters in a meter? ....(100)

Teaspoons in a tablespoon? .... (3)

Ounces in a pound? ....(16)

Pounds in a ton?.........................(2,000)

Cups in a pint? .... (2)

Pints in a quart? .... (2)

Quarts in a gallon? ....(4)

Millimeters in a meter? .... (1,000)

Years in a century? ....(100)

Years in a decade? ....(10)

Celsius freezing? ....(0°C)

Celsius boiling? ....(100°C)

Fahrenheit freezing? ....(32°F)

Fahrenheit boiling? ....(212°F)

Number with only 2 factors? .... (prime)

Perimeter? ....(add the sides)

Area? ....(length x width)

Volume? .... (length x width x height)

Area of parallelogram?..........................
.... (base x height)

Area of triangle? ....($\frac{1}{2}$ base x height)

Area of trapezoid?...................................
..................................($\frac{base_1 + base_2}{2} \times height$)

Surface area of a rectangular
prism? ....2(lw) + 2(wh) + 2(lh)

Area of a circle? ....(πr^2)

Circumference of a circle? ....(πd)

Triangle with no sides equal? ....
.... (scalene)

Triangle with 3 sides equal?...................
.... (equilateral)

Triangle with 2 sides equal? ....
.... (isosceles)

Distance across the middle of a circle?
.... (diameter)

Half of the diameter? .... (radius)

Figures with the same size
and shape? .... (congruent)

Figures with same shape,
different sizes? ....(similar)

Number occurring most often? ....
.... (mode)

Middle number? ....(median)

Answer in addition? ....(sum)

Answer in division? ....(quotient)

Answer in multiplication? ....(product)

Answer in subtraction? ......(difference)

Algebra I
Part B

Mathematics
3rd Edition

Answers to Lessons

	Lesson #1		Lesson #2		Lesson #3
1	243	**1**	$25x^4y^6z^8$	**1**	$m^{18}n^{12}$
2	$6 > x > -3$	**2**	32	**2**	nonagon
3	-145	**3**	$\dfrac{6b^2}{a^3c}$	**3**	6.34×10^9
4	32,600	**4**	$x = -14$	**4**	$12a^2 + 3a$
5	$12x^3 + 9x^2 - 24x$	**5**	132 cm^2	**5**	$-8x^4y^3z^2$
6	$m = \frac{7}{4}$	**6**	32°F	**6**	undefined
7	$\dfrac{32x^2}{5}$	**7**	$21\sqrt{xy}$	**7**	153.86 in^2
8	$12a + 2$	**8**	$5\frac{5}{7}$	**8**	$a = 25$
9	$\frac{x^2}{y^7}$	**9**	45	**9**	$3\sqrt{2} + \sqrt{3}$
10	22	**10**	$-42y^{11}$	**10**	$x^4 + x^2 - 12$
11	$9\frac{19}{20}$	**11**	$(3k - 5)(3k + 5)$	**11**	$7x^2y^3$
12	$64d^2 - 16$	**12**	0.0189	**12**	52
13	6 decades	**13**	$h \leq 9$	**13**	$\dfrac{-b \pm \sqrt{b^2 - 4ac}}{2a}$
14	$45b^{15}$	**14**	8.12×10^{-5}	**14**	$x = -112$
15	$6\sqrt{2}$	**15**	84	**15**	$\frac{3}{4}$
16	$(1, 2)$	**16**	isosceles	**16**	$16x^2 - 16x + 4$
17	$38\sqrt{3}$	**17**	$-6xy^3\sqrt{7xy}$	**17**	-23
18	$\dfrac{ab^2}{9}$	**18**	32	**18**	$y = \{1, 11, -19\}$
19	1	**19**	$\begin{pmatrix} 2 & -1 & 2 \\ 7 & 1 & -3 \end{pmatrix}$	**19**	$(y + 9)(y + 8)$
20	$13a^3 + 10a^2 - 9a + 1$	**20**	158 cm^2	**20**	$7x^3 - 9x^2 + 6x - 8$

	Lesson #4		Lesson #5		Lesson #6
1	$5\sqrt{2} - 4$	**1**	25%	**1**	$5x(x - 2)$
2	$(y + 5)(y - 3)$	**2**	$0.32,\ \frac{8}{25}$	**2**	3.8×10^{-6}
3	$(2, 3)$	**3**	145	**3**	$\frac{1}{h^5}$
4	$9x^3 - 21x^2 + 12x$	**4**	15	**4**	15
5	$\dfrac{a^2}{16b^3c^2}$	**5**	$x + 15$	**5**	$6c^3 - 24c^2 + 12c$
6	$x = 7$	**6**	$x = -15$	**6**	$t = 3$
7	$100\ \text{mm}^2$	**7**	$x \le 5$	**7**	$x = 75$
8	$a = 6$	**8**	$\dfrac{-b \pm \sqrt{b^2 - 4ac}}{2a}$	**8**	$16y^2 - 25$
9	\$302.40	**9**	$27a^6b^9$	**9**	-120
10	$64a^8b^4c^2$	**10**	$14\frac{3}{5}$	**10**	$a \ge 8$
11	37	**11**	0.000065	**11**	$9a^5$
12	$3\sqrt{5} + 2\sqrt{3}$	**12**	$3x^3 + 14x^2 + 11x - 12$	**12**	$(b - 9)(b + 3)$
13	178,014	**13**	40	**13**	64 quarts
14	$24x^7y^{20}$	**14**	$\dfrac{5y^2}{8x^5}$	**14**	$m = \frac{3}{4}$
15	6.5×10^{-4}	**15**	$y = \{-14, 2, -4\}$	**15**	25%
16	$x = -27$	**16**	$\frac{3}{10}$	**16**	$\frac{9}{49}$
17	$x = 60$	**17**	$\begin{pmatrix} 14 & -11 \\ -3 & 2 \end{pmatrix}$	**17**	$95\ \text{cm}^2$
18	5.43, 5.4, 5.05, 5.043	**18**	scalene	**18**	$(a - 4)(a + 4)$
19	$x \ge 9$	**19**	$(4, 3)$	**19**	$10x^4y^4\sqrt{6xy}$
20	$23x^3 - 7x^2 - 3x + 2$	**20**	$7a^3 + 7a^2 - 6a + 12$	**20**	$19x^2 - 8x + 2$

	Lesson #7		Lesson #8		Lesson #9
1	32	**1**	$30\sqrt{5}$	**1**	$-2 = y$
2	19	**2**	15	**2**	8.27×10^5
3	$x^2 - 4x - 12$	**3**	$(k - 8)(k + 8)$	**3**	$x = 15$
4	$5a^5b^7$	**4**	$V = \pi r^2 h$	**4**	$4ab(2a^2 + 4a^3b^2 - b)$
5	0.0029	**5**	42	**5**	$36\%, \frac{8}{25}$
6	$3 = y$	**6**	$\$1,026.00$	**6**	23.4
7	$4x^2yz$	**7**	8, 1	**7**	$12x^3 + 22x^2 + 17x + 12$
8	c^2d^3	**8**	$8x^2 + 16x + 6$	**8**	$y = mx + b$
9	$x \leq 8$	**9**	$x = 48$	**9**	$18n^9$
10	$\frac{1}{216}$	**10**	$\frac{1}{2}$	**10**	$(m - 10)(m + 4)$
11	$(a + 9)(a + 6)$	**11**	$a = 6$	**11**	102
12	slope $= -5$ y$-$int $= 2$	**12**	71,600	**12**	$6\frac{3}{7}$
13	-81	**13**	$\frac{10y^2}{x^3z^5}$	**13**	30
14	$6a^4\sqrt{2a}$	**14**	30%	**14**	33
15	95	**15**	1,300 cm	**15**	$\begin{pmatrix} 11 & -5 & -9 \\ 13 & 5 & 5 \end{pmatrix}$
16	$12\sqrt{3}$	**16**	$28a^{10}$	**16**	$12a^3 - 9a^2 + 15a$
17	7, 2	**17**	$m = 1$	**17**	$h \leq 6$
18	$c = -148$	**18**	$3x(x + 4)(x - 1)$	**18**	67%
19	-15	**19**	0, -4, -11, -31, -88	**19**	37.68 ft
20	$\sqrt{7}$	**20**	$5x^2 - 7$	**20**	$\frac{d^2}{c^{10}}$

	Lesson #10		Lesson #11		Lesson #12
1	$x^2 + 3x - 28$	**1**	46	**1**	$x^2 + 5x - 24$
2	3, 2	**2**	5.7×10^{-5}	**2**	$4 = x$
3	42	**3**	$24°$	**3**	215.6
4	$16x - 2$	**4**	$y = -5x + 26$	**4**	$20n^8$
5	48	**5**	$(2x - 1)(x + 3)$	**5**	3.1×10^{-5}
6	$c = -21$	**6**	$6a^2 - 22a - 8$	**6**	$c = 18$
7	0.2572	**7**	3	**7**	$3(2a^2 - 3a + 5)$
8	4×10^9	**8**	$36c^8d^{10}$	**8**	$x = 135$
9	$x = -28$	**9**	-34	**9**	$13\sqrt{5}$
10	42	**10**	31,680 feet	**10**	$16a + 8$
11	$x = 54$	**11**	$5\sqrt{5}$	**11**	$8x - 7$
12	$10a^6b^8$	**12**	80%	**12**	-74
13	1, -3	**13**	$\dfrac{a + 3}{a - 3}$	**13**	2
14	$48x^3$	**14**	$5a(a^2 - 2a + 3)$	**14**	complementary
15	zero	**15**	$(1, -1)$	**15**	$y = \{2, 10, -2\}$
16	$x = 75$	**16**	$\frac{1}{8}$	**16**	$\frac{2}{5}$
17	$x = 7$	**17**	$a = -6$	**17**	$\frac{1}{16}$
18	$10\frac{3}{8}$	**18**	$x^2 + x - 56$	**18**	k^{50}
19	$x = -25$	**19**	27	**19**	0.08, 8%
20	B(2, -5) C(-4, 0)	**20**	$\frac{1}{25}$	**20**	(7, 5)

	Lesson #13		Lesson #14		Lesson #15
1	$x = 35$	**1**	-148	**1**	$\dfrac{4y + 3}{6}$
2	24	**2**	$216x^6 y^{12}$	**2**	127
3	36%	**3**	zero	**3**	$16x^2 - 24x + 9$
4	-81	**4**	$5(2x^2 - x + 1)$	**4**	$\dfrac{a^2 c}{125 b^4}$
5	34,000	**5**	6	**5**	$\dfrac{9x^3}{20 y^2}$
6	$7a^3 + 31a^2 - 18a + 10$	**6**	$15a^2 + 39a + 18$	**6**	$y = mx + b$
7	$25a^6 b^4 c^8$	**7**	$\dfrac{a^3 c}{100 b^4}$	**7**	$3x^2 + 7x - 6$
8	$99\frac{19}{35}$	**8**	$C = d\pi$	**8**	0.2471
9	-234	**9**	$(d - 4)(d - 3)$	**9**	613,000
10	$25x^2 - 30x + 9$	**10**	17°	**10**	$(3y + 5)(3y - 5)$
11	74	**11**	equilateral	**11**	15%
12	$t = 1$	**12**	36,960 ft	**12**	$6(2b^3 - 3b^2 + 4)$
13	$\dfrac{4ac^3}{b^2}$	**13**	96 m²	**13**	$25c^4 d^6 f^8$
14	$(y - 7)(y - 2)$	**14**	$\frac{1}{3}$	**14**	$15 = x$
15	$x \geq 6$	**15**	$\frac{1}{64}$	**15**	$p = 158$
16	$9b^3 c^4$	**16**	212°F	**16**	60
17	$2\sqrt{3}$	**17**	13.95	**17**	$24x^6$
18	$\frac{x}{11} - 4$	**18**	6.28×10^{-4}	**18**	19
19	$\dfrac{x}{x + 3}$	**19**	20	**19**	$4\sqrt{3}$
20	$7a^3 - 8a^2 + 2a + 10$	**20**	$9a - 6$	**20**	$x = 56$

	Lesson #16		Lesson #17		Lesson #18
1	$x = 9$	**1**	$(y - 8)^2$	**1**	$\frac{1}{d^{21}}$
2	$-4x^4y^6$	**2**	80	**2**	$6x^2 + 21x - 12$
3	$x^2 + 3x - 18$	**3**	$5a^4 - 17a^3 + 6a^2 + 4a - 12$	**3**	$x = 63$
4	7.2×10^{-6}	**4**	$x = 36$	**4**	$(y + 7)(y + 2)$
5	$m = -1$	**5**	$3y^3 + 6y$	**5**	$x + 5$
6	236	**6**	157	**6**	$\frac{x + 2}{2x^2}$
7	$5\sqrt{2}$	**7**	$9a^8b^7\sqrt{2ab}$	**7**	-372
8	$\frac{x + 7}{x + 5}$	**8**	$3x + 7$	**8**	$c = -68$
9	$(a - 7)(a - 2)$	**9**	18	**9**	96
10	$12y\sqrt{y}$	**10**	$5x + 15$	**10**	$-4, 5$
11	$12d^3 - 20d^2$	**11**	$x = 63$	**11**	$\frac{b^2c}{a^4d^3}$
12	$\frac{m^6}{p^6}$	**12**	$\$963.00$	**12**	$10a + 1$
13	$\frac{5}{8}$	**13**	$y = 10 \quad y = -4$	**13**	$b = -16$
14	254 m^2	**14**	$\frac{x^2}{y^7}$	**14**	$x = 6$
15	$\frac{1}{a^5}$	**15**	$60x^3y^2z^4$	**15**	45
16	80	**16**	90	**16**	0.000817
17	$A = \pi r^2$	**17**	$5(x - 5)$	**17**	71%
18	$(17, 5)$	**18**	$-7 = m$	**18**	
19	$m = 15$	**19**	9.1×10^7	**19**	$0.06, 6\%$
20	$A(-5, 5) \quad C(2, 5)$	**20**	$25x^2 - 6x - 4$	**20**	75 basketballs

	Lesson #19		Lesson #20		Lesson #21
1	$m = 1$	**1**	$\frac{8}{9}$	**1**	$-11 < x < -5$
2	$x = 153$	**2**	$6x^6\sqrt{5x}$	**2**	96
3	$\frac{x}{5} - 6$	**3**	$(4a + 1)(a - 3)$	**3**	$y < 10 \quad y > -4$
4	86	**4**	0.000032	**4**	$16a^2 + 48a + 36$
5	$\dfrac{x + 9}{x + 1}$	**5**	$\dfrac{4a^2b}{5}$	**5**	$8x^2 - 2x - 15$
6	46	**6**	$x^2 + 13x + 40$	**6**	91,600,000
7	$(c - 8)(c + 7)$	**7**	14	**7**	$8x^3 - 11x^2 + 11x - 10$
8	$\frac{3}{2x}$	**8**	$x^{12}y^{16}z^8$	**8**	$9d^4 - 15d^3 + 21d$
9	$16x^3 - 8x^2 - 14x + 6$	**9**	90	**9**	$y = mx + b$
10	$12a(3a^2 + a - 2)$	**10**	$24a^6$	**10**	scalene
11	36.709	**11**	$y \geq -12$	**11**	$(s - 7)(s - 4)$
12	38%, 0.56, $\frac{3}{5}$	**12**	$10a + 10$	**12**	$\dfrac{6x^4}{y^5z^3}$
13	3,617.28 m³	**13**	$3a^2b^2c^2$	**13**	$24x^{16}\sqrt{5}$
14	3.5×10^{10}	**14**	$\frac{x^2}{y^3}$	**14**	0.2762
15	100°C	**15**	$\frac{1}{32}$	**15**	$x = -6$
16	$2 = a$	**16**	$y = 16 \quad y = -4$	**16**	57
17	$3m^3n^2\sqrt{7mn}$	**17**	$x = 125$	**17**	36
18	$>$	**18**	56.52 in.	**18**	$x = 91$
19	$39\frac{1}{15}$	**19**	$x = 26$	**19**	45
20	$5x$	**20**	$3x^2$	**20**	$\frac{4}{3b}$

	Lesson #22		Lesson #23		Lesson #24
1	$6a^3 + 26a^2 + 11a + 12$	1	$2 = x$	1	$x = 4$
2	16,000 grams	2	$5a^3b^7$	2	$\frac{1}{d^{12}}$
3	9.9×10^4	3	-178	3	-127
4	$y = -17$	4	$4x^3 - 11x^2 + 8x - 4$	4	$x = 18$
5	360 m^2	5	slope = 7 y int = -3	5	26
6	$5x - 6$	6	24	6	$(t - 3)^2$
7	$\frac{x^4z^3}{8}$	7	$(x - 12)(x - 4)$	7	$21m^2 - 35m$
8	-60	8	$18a^7b^4\sqrt{5ab}$	8	$y = x - 4$
9	$(c + 7)(c - 7)$	9	$A = \pi r^2$	9	$1 = h$
10	f^{25}	10	0.0000075	10	7.4×10^{11}
11	15	11	$20a^3 + 30a^2 - 35a$	11	$(6, 13)$
12	$6c^2\sqrt{7c}$	12	$3x$	12	$\frac{5}{128}, \frac{3}{40}$
13	$h = -125$	13	$\begin{pmatrix} 9 & -5 & -5 \\ 5 & 4 & -6 \end{pmatrix}$	13	$40x^6$
14	$8b(b^2 - 2b + 3)$	14	28	14	11%
15	50%	15	81	15	$10 < c < 12$
16	$\frac{2a - 4}{a + 5}$	16	$x = 112$	16	$5r(1 + 3r^2 + 5r)$
17	$y = \{1, -9, 7\}$	17	$x = 6$	17	$\frac{-b \pm \sqrt{b^2 - 4ac}}{2a}$
18	$V = lwh$	18	$\frac{2xy^2}{9}$	18	$6a^2 + a - 1$
19	0.35, 35%	19	$\frac{5b}{7}$	19	$4x$
20	$x = 9$	20	$32a + 12$	20	$-\frac{(4 + y)}{y - 1}$

	Lesson #25		Lesson #26		Lesson #27
1	-66	**1**	$-31, -29, -16, -5, 0$	**1**	$x = 7$
2	$\frac{3}{4}$	**2**	$h = 15 \quad h = -7$	**2**	$x^2 - 5x - 36$
3	$12s^3 + 18s^2 - 2s - 8$	**3**	$x \le 3$	**3**	$(y - 8)(y - 2)$
4	$(x + 4)(x + 3)$	**4**	46	**4**	44
5	$x = 140$	**5**	$\frac{3}{2}$	**5**	$y = 4$
6	$10y^2 + 6y$	**6**	19	**6**	$8x^5$
7	6.62×10^{-6}	**7**	$x - 8$	**7**	zero
8	$40x^6$	**8**	$1,700,000,000$	**8**	$\frac{9d^3}{c^2}$
9	$16c^4 + 24c^3 - 40c^2$	**9**	$10\frac{2}{7}$	**9**	-33
10	36 cups	**10**	$(a - 8)(a + 8)$	**10**	$a^2 + b^2 = c^2$
11	$x = -36$	**11**	$-9 = c$	**11**	$x^4 y^3 \sqrt{xy}$
12	$49a^{10}b^6c^4$	**12**	$6x^2 + x - 2$	**12**	$C = 15$ cm
13	$0.36, 36\%$	**13**	$-20x^4 \sqrt{x}$	**13**	90%
14	$x = 1$	**14**	3.738	**14**	67%
15	$24x^6y^4$	**15**	$18a^2 - 4$	**15**	hypotenuse
16	$80a^3b^2c^2$	**16**	$\frac{5c}{8d^2}$	**16**	6.23×10^8
17	$\frac{-15y}{14}$	**17**	$(1, 0)$	**17**	$3\sqrt{3}$
18	$11\sqrt{7}$	**18**	$\frac{2}{3}$	**18**	$36p^3 - 30p^2 + 12p$
19	$101\frac{19}{45}$	**19**	$a^3 + 15a^2 + 75a + 125$	**19**	$10x^3 + 8x^2 + 12$
20	$\frac{3x}{x - 3}$	**20**	$\frac{11a + 19}{36a}$	**20**	$\frac{3a^2 + 8a - 10}{3a - 2}$

	Lesson #28		Lesson #29		Lesson #30
1	$\frac{1}{t^{40}}$	**1**	B(–5, 6) D(3, –4)	**1**	$x \geq 3$
2	$a^2 + b^2 = c^2$	**2**	75	**2**	$y = mx + b$
3	$4\frac{3}{7}$	**3**	undefined	**3**	$-30x^3y^3$
4	$x = 36$	**4**	$a^2 + b^2 = c^2$	**4**	$x^2 + 11x + 28$
5	0.0032	**5**	$(2c + 1)(c - 3)$	**5**	$a^2 + b^2 = c^2$
6	64.419	**6**	$\frac{-1}{10x^2}$	**6**	–23
7	$10a^4$	**7**	$12b^3 + 16b^2 - 12b + 8$	**7**	$\frac{y}{2x}$
8	$(x - 4)^2$	**8**	$\frac{y}{16x^5}$	**8**	$81b^{12}c^8d^{16}$
9	0.40	**9**	36,960 feet	**9**	$10a^2b^5\sqrt{5ab}$
10	$12a^2 + 4a$	**10**	$\frac{3x^4}{2}$	**10**	$\frac{29x - 27}{12}$
11	$12a^2bc^3\sqrt{ac}$	**11**	$6x^2 - 23x + 15$	**11**	$\frac{14x}{2}$
12	$15x^2 - x - 6$	**12**	$15x^2y^4\sqrt{2}$	**12**	$\frac{1}{216}$
13	59°	**13**	$x = -39$	**13**	$4x^2(2x^2 - 3x + 5)$
14	$\frac{-4a}{5}$	**14**	$\frac{a}{5}$	**14**	$t^2 + 8t + 16$
15	10	**15**	$6y + 2$	**15**	24
16	$a = -1$ $a = -9$	**16**	4.9×10^{-3}	**16**	–20
17	$\frac{a^2 + 2a + 2}{a + 1}$	**17**	$43\frac{21}{40}$	**17**	5,300,000
18	$y = 7x - 28$	**18**	$4 > x$	**18**	$b = 15$
19	$y = \{9, -15, 13\}$	**19**	$b = 20$	**19**	$(x - 7)(x - 8)$
20	$x = 99$	**20**	–34	**20**	$0.6x^2 + 0.3x - 1.4$